CW00551937

MATHEMATICS

Mechanics
Unit M2

Professor W E Williams
& Dr S Y Barham

AS/A LEVEL

WJEC AS/A Level Mathematics
Mechanics Unit M2

Published by the Welsh Joint Education Committee
245 Western Avenue, Cardiff, CF5 2YX

First published 2001

Printed by Hackman Printers Ltd
Clydach Vale, Tonypandy, Rhondda, CF40 2XX

ISBN: 1 86085 464 8

FOREWORD

This book covers the requirements in Unit M2 of the new WJEC syllabus and also most of the topics required in the Unit MS. Statics, which is required in Unit MS is covered in the M3 book.
The treatment of vectors is confined to those aspects which are relevant to Mechanics.

We are indebted to a number of teachers who made various suggestions. In particular, we extend our thanks to Kevin McGuire, John Langley and Elwyn Davies who checked and sent us answers to exercises in the old M1 book, which are also used in this book.

Every effort has been made to eliminate errors present in previous versions. However, any that remain are the responsibility of the authors.

CONTENTS

Chapter 1

Rectilinear Motion

After working through this chapter you should

- be able, given one of displacement, velocity or acceleration as a function of time, to find the other two.
- be able to solve simple problems involving forces dependent on time.

1.1 Problems needing the use of calculus

You have already learnt in M1, chapter 4, how to solve problems involving motion in a straight line under constant acceleration. In this chapter, problems where acceleration depends on time will be considered.

The basic relations between displacement x, velocity v and acceleration a are

$$v = \frac{dx}{dt}$$

$$a = \frac{dv}{dt} = \frac{d^2x}{dt^2}$$

The simplest types of problems that can arise are those when x is given in terms of t and it is required to find v and/or a, or v is given in terms of t and a has to be found. Solutions to problems of this type only require differentiation of the given quantities.

A slightly more complicated class of problems is that where a is given in terms of t and x has to be found. In these cases, the given quantities have to be integrated with respect to time. Every integration produces a constant of integration so that values of x and/or v must be known for some values of t.
In dynamics, as you will find in the next chapter, force is directly proportional to acceleration. Therefore problems involving the action of forces normally mean having to find v and/or x from a given acceleration. In practical circumstances the acceleration

may not be a function of t only but may depend on x and/or v. Problems of this type are harder to solve and will be considered in M3.

Example 1.1

The displacement of a particle at time t s is $(t^3 + 4t^2 + 6t)$ m; find its velocity and acceleration.

Differentiation with respect to t gives the velocity as $(3t^2 + 8t + 6)$ ms^{-1} and a further differentiation gives the acceleration as $(6t + 8)$ ms^{-2}.

Example 1.2

Find the acceleration of a particle at time t s given that its velocity is $t \sin 3t$ ms^{-1}.

The acceleration is found by differentiating the velocity with respect to time. In this case the product rule for differentiation has to be used, so the acceleration is $(\sin 3t + 3t \cos 3t)$ ms^{-2}.

Example 1.3

Find the position of a particle at time t s given that its acceleration is t ms^{-2} and that at time $t = 0$ the displacement of the particle from a fixed point and the velocity of the particle are 3 m and 6 ms^{-1}, respectively.

In this case

$$\frac{dv}{dt} = t,$$

where the velocity is v ms^{-1}, and integrating this equation with respect to t gives $v = \frac{1}{2}t^2$ + constant. Since the velocity is 6 ms^{-1} at time $t = 0$ this gives the constant to be 6. Therefore

$$\frac{dx}{dt} = \frac{1}{2}t^2 + 6,$$

where x m denotes the displacement. Integrating this equation with respect to t gives $x = \frac{1}{6}t^3 + 6t$ + constant. Since the displacement is 3 m at time $t = 0$ substitution of $t = 0$ into the expression for x gives the constant as 3.

Therefore the displacement is $(\frac{1}{6}t^3 + 6t + 3)$m.

An alternative method which would avoid introducing a constant is to integrate between $t = 0$ and $t = t$, this gives

$$[x]_{\text{at t}} - [x]_{\text{at } t=0} = \frac{1}{6}t^3 + 6t,$$

substituting for $[x]_{\text{at } t=0}$ as 3 gives the previous result.

The method to be used in problems where the acceleration is given in terms of t essentially consists, as in the above example, of two steps:-

(i) Integrate with respect to t to find v, remembering to introduce an arbitrary constant or to integrate between limits if v is given for some value of t.

(ii) Integrate the expression for v to find x, remembering to introduce a second constant or to integrate between appropriate limits if possible. Then find the constants using the given initial conditions.

Example 1.4

A particle moving under an acceleration of t^2 ms^{-2} at time t s has a velocity of 1 ms^{-1} when $t = 3$ and its displacement from a given point is 4 m when $t = 12$. Find its displacement from the given point when $t = 9$.

The velocity v ms^{-1} at time t s satisfies the equation

$$\frac{dv}{dt} = t^2.$$

Integrating this with respect to t gives $v = \frac{1}{3}t^3 + c$, where c is a constant. Substituting $v = 1$ and $t = 3$ in this equation gives $1 = 9 + c$, so that $c = -8$. Therefore

$$\frac{dx}{dt} = \frac{1}{3}t^3 - 8,$$

where x m denotes the displacement. This equation needs to be integrated again. One method is to integrate directly introducing another arbitrary constant and find this by using the value of x at $t = 12$. The alternative, which is the one used here, is to integrate from $t = 12$ to $t = t$.

This gives

$$[x]_{\text{at } t} - [x]_{\text{at } t = 0} = \frac{1}{12}\left(t^4 - 12^4\right) - 8(t - 12)$$

Substituting for the value of x at $t = 12$ and evaluating x at $t = 9$ gives the displacement from $x = 4$ at time $t = 12$ as -1157.25 m. So the actual displacement is $-1157.25 + 4 = -1153.25$m.

In slightly more complicated problems, the form of the acceleration may differ from one time interval to another. In such cases, the general solutions should be found for each of the time intervals separately and the constants determined from the given conditions. The values of x and v at the end of one time interval may be needed to work out the appropriate constants in the succeeding interval.

Example 1.5

A particle starts from rest with acceleration $(2 + 6t)$ ms^{-2} at time t s and after 2 s the acceleration changes to the constant value of 14 ms^{-2} and is then maintained at this value. Find the distance covered in the first 5 s of the motion.

For the first 2 s,

$$\frac{dv}{dt} = 2 + 6t.$$

Integrating with respect to t gives $v = 2t + 3t^2 + b$, where b is a constant. Substituting the values at $t = 0$ gives $b = 0$ and so $v = 2t + 3t^2$. A second integration with respect to t gives

$$x = t^2 + t^3 + c,$$

where c is a further constant. At $t = 0$, $x = 0$, and so $c = 0$ and so $x = t^2 + t^3$. So after 2 s the particle has velocity 16 ms^{-1} and has covered a distance of 12 m. It now moves with a constant acceleration of 14 ms^{-2} with initial speed 16 ms^{-1} for a further time of $(5 - 2)$ s = 3 s. Using an equation for constant acceleration gives

$$s = 16 \times 3 + \frac{1}{2} \times 14 \times 9 = 111.$$

Therefore the required displacement is (12 + 111) m = 123 m.

Exercises 1.1

The following questions refer to a particle moving along Ox, where x m denotes the displacement from O of the particle at time t s, and v ms^{-1} and a ms^{-2} denote the velocity and acceleration in the sense of increasing x, at time t s.

1 $x = 7t^4 + 2t^3 + 5$, find a.

2 $v = 3t^3 + 4t^2 + 1$, find a.

3 $a = 24t^2 + 18t + 2$, $v = 2$ and $x = 0$ when $t = 0$; find x.

4 $a = 20t^3 + 12t^2$, $x = 1$ when $t = 0$, $v = 6$ when $t = 1$; find x.

5 $a = e^{-t}$, $x = 2$ and $v = 4$ when $t = 0$; find x.

6 $a = 6t$ when $0 \le t \le 1$, $a = 6$ when $t \ge 1$, $v = 1$ and $x = 0$ when $t = 0$; find x for $t = 1$ and $t = 2$.

7 $a = 24t^2 + 6$ when $0 \le t \le 1$, $a = 30t$, $t \ge 1$, $v = 2$ and $x = 1$ when $t = 0$; find x for $t > 1$.

1.2 Forces dependent on time

In practical situations, forces acting will not be constant. For example, even for a car working at a constant rate the force will depend on velocity, and it is often not very straightforward to find the position and velocity given the force. You have already seen that finding the displacement from the force is not difficult when the force is constant. The other case which can be done fairly easily is that when the force is known in terms of t. The equation of motion $F = ma$ gives the acceleration in terms of t and therefore x and v can be found exactly as in 1.1.

Example 1.6

A particle of mass 0.4kg is moving under the action of a force in the positive x-direction which at time t s is $4 \exp \frac{t}{4}$ N and which acts for $0 \le t \le 4$. At time $t = 0$ the particle is at rest at the point $x = 0$. Find its velocity and displacement when $t = 4$.

If v ms^{-1} denotes the velocity in the positive x-direction, then Newton's second law gives

$$0.4 \frac{dv}{dt} = 4 \exp \frac{t}{4}.$$

Integrating this equation from $t = 0$ to $t = t$ gives

$$v = 40 \left(\exp \frac{t}{4} - 1 \right),$$

where the condition $v = 0$ at $t = 0$ has been used. Substituting $t = 4$ gives the velocity at $t = 4$ as 68.73 ms^{-1}.

Therefore $$\frac{dx}{dt} = 40 \left(\exp \frac{t}{4} - 1 \right),$$

where x m denotes the displacement at time t s, and integrating this equation from $t = 0$ to $t = t$ gives

$$x = 40 \left(4 \exp \frac{t}{4} - t \right) - 40(4)$$

where the condition $x = 0$ at $t = 0$ has been used. Substituting $t = 4$ gives the displacement at $t = 4$ as 115m.

Exercises 1.2

1. A particle of mass m kg moves in a straight line under the action of a force acting along the same straight line and which at time t s is $m(2 + 6t)$N. The particle is moving at 20ms^{-1} when $t = 2$. Calculate the speed of the particle when $t = 0$.
2. A body of mass 2 kg starts from rest at O and moves along the x-axis under the action of a force $(6t - t^2)$N acting in the positive x direction. What is the speed of the body (i) after 3s, (ii) after 9s from the start?
3. A particle of mass m kg starts from rest at the origin and moves in a straight line under the action of a force along this line, which at time t s is $0.2me^{2t}$ N. Find the velocity of the particle when $t = 3$, and the distance of the particle from the origin when $t = 2$.
4. A particle of mass m moves up a line of greatest slope of a smooth incline plane, the angle α made by this line of greatest slope with the horizontal being such that

$\tan\alpha = \frac{3}{4}$. There is a force acting on the particle up this line of greatest slope which at time t s is given by $m(12-3t)$N. Find the velocity acquired when starting from rest in (i) 2s, (ii) t s. Find the distance travelled in 3s from rest.

Miscellaneous Exercises 1

1 A particle P moves along the x-axis so that its velocity at time t s is v ms^{-1} where

$$v = 9t^2 - 4t + 1.$$

Given that P is at the origin when $t = 0$, find

(a) the distance of P from the origin when $t = 1$,

(b) the acceleration of P when $t = 1$.

2 A particle moves along a straight line so that its acceleration at time t seconds is $(6t - 8)$ ms^{-2}. At $t = 0$ seconds the particle passes through the fixed point O with a velocity of 4 ms^{-1}. Find

(i) the distance from O of the point where the particle first comes to instantaneous rest,

(ii) the total time T seconds taken by the particle to return to the starting point,

(iii) the greatest speed of the particle for $0 < t < T$.

3 A particle moves in a straight line so that its speed at time t s is inversely proportional to $(t + 3)$, and when $t = 2$ s, the particle has a retardation of 4/25 ms^{-2}. Given that the particle is at O at time $t = 0$, find its distance from O when $t = 1$.

4 The acceleration, at time t, of a particle moving in a straight line is $k \sin pt$, where k and p are constants. At time $t = 0$ the particle is at the point O and moving with velocity u. Show that its velocity at any subsequent time is

$$u + \frac{k}{p}(1 - \cos pt).$$

Show that, for $u = 0$, the particle first comes to instantaneous rest after travelling a distance of $\frac{2\pi k}{p^2}$.

5 A particle, moving in a straight line, starts from rest at time $t = 0$ s, and at time t s its velocity v ms^{-1} is given by

$$v = 3t(t-4) \text{ for } 0 \le t \le 5, \quad v = 75/t \quad 5 \le t \le k,$$

where k is a constant.

(i) Sketch the velocity-time diagram for the particle for $0 \le t \le k$.

(ii) Find the range of values of t for which the acceleration of the particle is positive.

(iii) Show that the **total** distance covered by the particle in the interval $0 \le t \le 5$ is 39 metres.

(iv) Given that the distance covered by the particle in the interval $5 \le t \le k$ is also 39 metres, find, to 2 significant figures, the value of k.

6 In order to model the final stages of the motion of a bird it is assumed that its speed is $(a + bt)$ ms^{-1}, where a and b are constants. The speed of the bird when $t = 0$ is 4 ms^{-1} and it comes to rest when $t = 3$. Find the values of a and b.
A more refined model is then sought which is such that the acceleration of the bird is zero when it comes to rest. Assuming that in this case, $v = p + qt + rt^2$, where p, q and r are constants, find the values of these constants.
Determine, for this model, the distance travelled by the bird in the last three seconds of its flight.

7 A particle P of mass 0.2 kg is acted on by a variable force so that its velocity in ms^{-1} at time t s is $16 - t^2$. Find the distance covered by P from time $t = 0$ until it comes to rest instantaneously. Find also the force acting on the particle at time t s.

8 Two bodies of mass 1 kg and 2 kg, initially at the points A and B respectively, start from rest at $t = 0$ and move along the horizontal straight line AB. The first is acted on by a force of $(6t + 2)$N towards B and the second by a force of $2(12t^2 + 16)$N towards A. Find

(a) the speed of each body after 1 second,

(b) the distances covered by each body during the first second.

Given that the bodies collide after 1 second, find the distance AB.

9 An electric train of mass M kg moves from rest along a straight level track. The tractive force of the motor, initially P N, decreases at a constant rate with time to R N over a period of T s and then remains constant at R N. The total resistance to motion is R N. Show that the acceleration a of the train at time t s after it starts to move is given, for $0 \leq t \leq T$, by

$$Ma = P + (R - P)\frac{t}{T} - R.$$

Find the maximum speed achieved by the train and the distance it travels before reaching that speed.

Find the power developed by the motor at time (i) $\frac{T}{2}$, (ii) $\frac{3T}{2}$.

10 A car of mass 1000 kg moves along a horizontal road with acceleration proportional to the cube root of the time t seconds after starting from rest. When $t = 27$, the speed of the car is 8 ms^{-1}. Find the rate at which the engine driving the car is working when $t = 64$. Frictional resistances may be neglected.

Chapter 2

Work, Energy and Power

After working through this chapter you should

- be able to calculate the work done by constant forces and those dependent only on position,
- know what is meant by kinetic energy, potential energy and power,
- be able to use the work-energy principle to find the work done by a force,
- know when the total mechanical energy is conserved and use the principle of conservation of mechanical energy to solve simple problems,
- be able to calculate the power necessary for engines such as water pumps to carry out their tasks.

2.1 Work done by a constant force

You will probably connect the word work with something which requires effort, for example if you push a wheelbarrow up a hill, or just cycle up a hill, you will feel that you have done some work. In Mechanics it is possible to give a precise definition of work which is, in fact, consistent with this general idea of expending effort. The simplest definition is for the case when the force is constant.

The work done by a constant force moving a particle along a line is the product of the distance moved by the particle and the component of the force in the direction of motion.

The work done by a force of 1 newton moving through 1 metre is the unit of work and is called the joule (J).

The work done can be positive or negative according as to whether the force is acting towards, or away from, the direction in which the particle is moved.

Example 2.1

Find the work done by a horizontal force of magnitude 30 N which pushes a heavy parcel a distance of 4 m along a smooth floor.

The work is the product of the distance and the component of force in the direction of motion and is therefore 30×4 J = 120 J.

Example 2.2

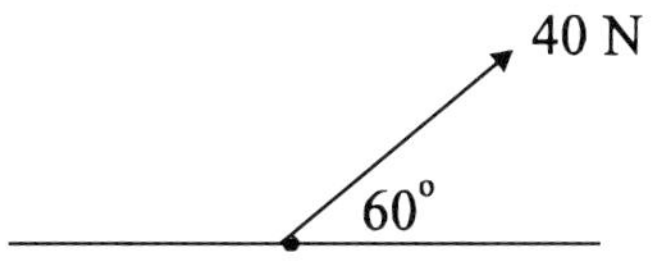

The diagram shows a particle on a horizontal wire being pulled along by a constant force of magnitude 40 N inclined at an angle of 60° to the wire. Find the work done by the force in moving the particle a distance of 0.4 m along the wire.
The component of force along the wire is $40 \cos 60^\circ$N = 20 N and therefore the work done is 20×0.4 J = 8 J.

Sometimes it is not the work done by a force that is required but the work done against it and you have to be clear as to which you are calculating. For example if a parcel of mass m is lifted a vertical distance h then the work done by gravity is $-mgh$, since the component of gravity in the direction of the motion of the particle is $-mg$. In order to find the work that has to be done in the lifting, it is assumed that the lifting is carried out extremely slowly at a constant speed so that the total force acting is zero and the lifting force therefore exactly balances the force of gravity. The magnitude of the lifting force is therefore mg and the work done by the lifting force is mgh. For a wheelbarrow moving up a hill the force of friction and the component of the weight along the hill are both in the opposite direction to the motion and so the work done by them is negative. If the wheelbarrow is moving at a constant speed, then the pushing force just balances the other forces at all times and the work done by it is minus the work done by friction and gravity. In general the work done against a particular force is taken to be minus the work done by the force.

Example 2.3

A particle of mass 0.5 kg is pulled a distance of 4 m, at a constant speed, up a slope inclined at an angle α to the horizontal, where $\tan \alpha = \frac{3}{4}$. The pulling force acts parallel to a line of greatest slope of the plane. The coefficient of friction between the particle and the plane is 0.5. Find the work done in this motion by the pulling force.

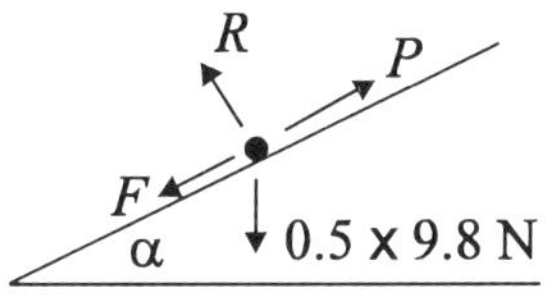

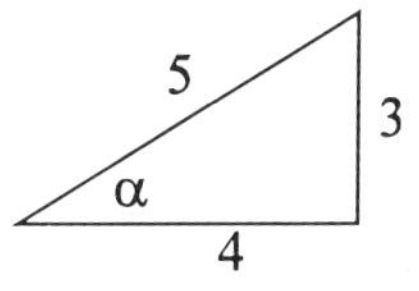

The left hand diagram diagram shows the forces acting on the particle with F, R and P denoting the magnitudes of the friction force, the normal reaction and the pulling force, respectively. The reaction of the plane does no work since its component in the direction of motion is zero, similarly it is only the component of the weight along the plane that does work. There are two ways of carrying out the calculation. One way is to find the work done by the friction and the work done by gravity separately and add them together. The work done by the pulling force is then minus this work. The other way is to say, since the particle is moving at a constant speed and has therefore no acceleration, that the force acting along the plane is equal in magnitude but opposite in direction to the components of friction and gravity along the plane, and work out the work done by this force. This second method is the one that will be used. The reaction is found by resolving perpendicular to the plane and is $0.5 \times 9.8 \times \cos\alpha$ N. The right hand diagram above shows that $\cos\alpha = \frac{4}{5}$ and therefore the reaction is 3.92 N and the force of friction is 1.96 N. The component of the weight down the plane is $0.5 \times 9.8 \times \sin\alpha = 2.94$ N. The total pulling force is therefore $(2.94 + 1.96)$ N $= 4.9$ N. The work done is therefore 4.9×4 J $= 19.6$ J.

Before calculating work done you should check that the force is constant before multiplying it by the distance moved. This method only makes sense for constant force. For forces which vary with position you need to use the definition in the following section.

Exercises 2.1

1 Find the work done by a horizontal force of magnitude 2 N pushing a particle a distance of 0.8 m along a horizontal surface.

2 A climber of mass 55 kg, climbing at a constant speed, does 1000 J of work. Find the distance climbed.

3 A parcel of mass 5 kg is lifted, at a constant speed, through a height of 5 m. Find, modelling the parcel as a particle, the work done against gravity.

4 A particle of mass 0.2 kg is pulled at a constant speed of 5 ms^{-1} along a rough horizontal surface. Given that the coefficient of friction is 0.3, find the work done against friction in 4 s.

5 A particle of mass 0.3 kg is pulled at a constant speed up a smooth plane inclined at an angle of 20° to the horizontal. Find the work done against gravity in moving the particle a distance of 3 m up the plane.

6 A packing case is pulled a distance of 4 m at a constant speed across a horizontal floor by a rope attached to it and inclined at an angle of 40° to the horizontal.

Given that the total work done by the pulling force is 80 J, find the tension in the rope.

7 A toboggan of mass 20 kg is pulled at a constant speed a distance of 12 m up a snowy slope inclined at an angle of 20° to the horizontal. The coefficient of friction between the toboggan and the snow is 0.6. Find

(i) the work done against gravity,

(ii) the work done against friction.

Given that the toboggan is being pulled by a rope attached to its front, find the tension in the rope for the two cases when

(a) the rope is parallel to the slope,

(b) the rope is at an angle of 45° to the slope.

8 A particle of mass 5 kg is pulled with constant speed up a plane inclined at an angle α to the horizontal, where $\sin\alpha = \frac{3}{5}$. The coefficient of friction between the plane and the particle is $\frac{1}{3}$. Given that the pulling force acts along a line of greatest slope, find the work done in moving the particle a distance of 10 m.

9 A man and bicycle are of total mass 100 kg. He travels, at a constant speed, a distance of 1 km up a hill inclined at an angle α to the horizontal, where $\sin\alpha = \frac{1}{20}$. The other resistances acting on him and directly opposing his motion total 20 N. Find the total work done by the cyclist.

10 The cyclist in the previous question is travelling at a constant speed down a hill inclined at an angle α to the horizontal where $\sin\alpha = \frac{1}{160}$ and does 1200 J of work in travelling a distance of 400 m. Find, assuming that it is constant, the total resistance to his motion.

2.2 Work done by a force dependent only on position

If a force is not constant, but depends on position, then it is not sensible to define work as force times distance since you would not know at what point to calculate the force! In order to find a more sensible definition it is necessary to have a graphical interpretation of work.

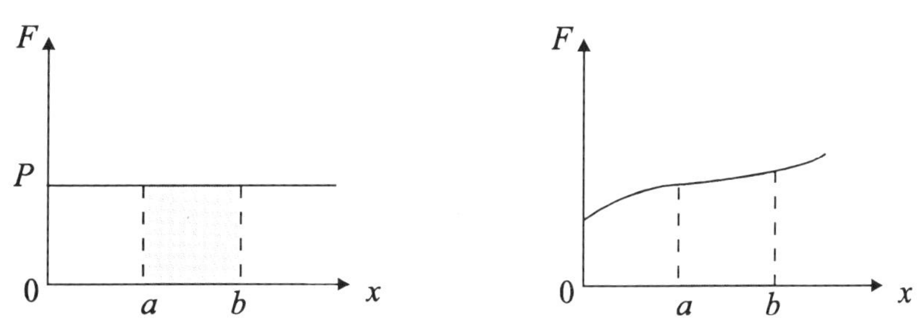

If the component of force in the positive x direction is denoted by F then the left hand diagram shows the graph of F for a constant force of magnitude P and the right hand diagram a possible graph when F is not constant but depends on position i.e. x. If F has the constant value P, then the work done moving from $x = a$ to $x = b$ is $P(b - a)$; this is the area under the straight line in the left hand diagram. Therefore a sensible definition of the work done moving from $x = a$ to $x = b$ when F depends on x would be the area under the curve in the right hand diagram between the lines $x = a$ and $x = b$. This is the definition used, and since the area under a curve can be represented as an integral, the work done in a displacement of the point of application of the force from $x = a$ to $x = b$ is defined as

$$\int_a^b F(x)\,\mathrm{d}x.$$

This definition, as has been shown above, reduces to the original definition when the force is constant.

The integral definition is actually valid for all forces but, when the force depends on other variables such as t and v, the integral is not easy to evaluate.

Example 2.4

When the displacement of a particle from the origin is x m, the force acting on it is of magnitude $(10 + 4e^{-x})$ N and acts in the positive x direction. Find the work done when the particle moves from $x = 0$ to $x = 1$.

The work done is

$$\int_0^1 \left(10 + 4e^{-x}\right)\mathrm{d}x \text{ J} = 10 - 4\left(e^{-1} - 1\right) \text{ J} = 14 - 4e^{-1} \text{ J}$$

Exercises 2.2

1 When a particle P is at a point on the positive x-axis at a distance of x m from the origin, the force in the positive x direction is of magnitude $4x$ N. Find the work done by the force when

(i) the particle moves from the point $x = 1$ to $x = 2$,

(ii) the particle moves from the point $x = 4$ to $x = 3$.

2 When the displacement of a particle from the origin is x m, the force in the positive x direction acting on it is denoted by $F(x)$ N. Find the work done in moving the particle from the point $x = a$ to the point $x = b$ when

(i) $F = 4x^3 + 3x^2$, $a = 1$, $b = 2$,

(ii) $F = 3 + 4e^{-x}$, $a = 0$, $b = 1$,

(iii) $F = \dfrac{4}{x^2}$, $a = 2$, $b = 4$.

3 A truck is pulled along a straight horizontal track by a horizontal force whose magnitude, when the truck is at a distance of x m from its starting point, is $(8 - \frac{x}{20})$ N. Find the work done as the truck moves a distance of 100 m.

2.3 Work done by the tension in an elastic string

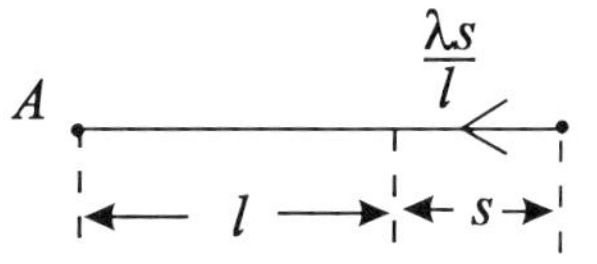

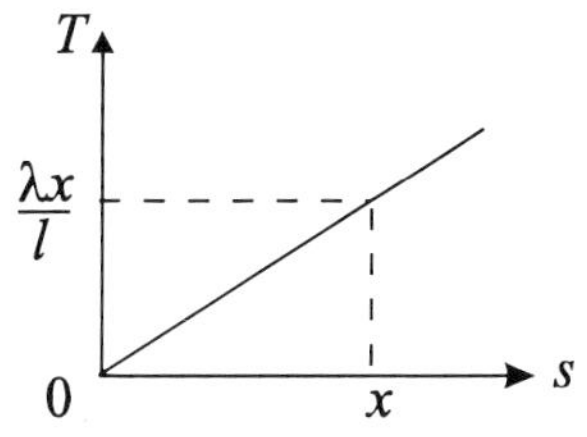

If an elastic string has one end fixed at a point A and the other end is extended a distance s beyond its natural length, then Hooke's law shows that the tension T is of magnitude $\frac{\lambda s}{l}$ where λ is the elastic modulus and l is its natural length. This tension acts away from the extended end as shown in the left hand diagram and therefore its component towards the fixed end is $\frac{\lambda s}{l}$. The right hand diagram shows the variation of tension with extension s. The magnitude of the work done by the tension when the string is extended from $s = 0$ to $s = x$ is therefore the area under the straight line between $s = 0$ and $s = x$; this is $\frac{\lambda x^2}{2l}$. Since the tension is directed away from the direction of extension, the work done by it in the extension is $-\frac{\lambda x^2}{2l}$. The same result is obtained by integrating the force in the direction of the extension, i.e. $-\frac{\lambda s}{l}$, from $s = 0$ and $s = x$, this gives

$$-\int_0^x \frac{\lambda s}{l} ds = -\frac{\lambda x^2}{2l}.$$

The particular letter used for the variable of integration is not very important, it is what is known as a dummy variable, but it is better, and avoids confusion, not to use as a variable of integration a variable which occurs in one of the limits.
Therefore the work done against the tension in extending an elastic string a distance x is $\frac{\lambda x^2}{2l}$ and this can also be shown, in a similar way, to be true when a spring is compressed a distance x.

The work done against the tension in increasing the extension of an elastic spring from a to b is

$$\int_a^b \frac{\lambda s}{l}\,\mathrm{d}s = \frac{\lambda}{2l}\left(b^2 - a^2\right).$$

Exercises 2.3

Find the work done in extending an elastic string of natural length l m and modulus λ N a distance of x m from its unstretched length when

1 $l = 2,\ \lambda = 100, x = 0.2.$

2 $l = 3,\ \lambda = 300, x = 0.4.$

3 $l = 2.5,\ \lambda = 500, x = \frac{l}{4}.$

Find the work done in increasing the extension of an elastic string of natural length l m and modulus λ N from a m to b m when

4 $l = 2,\ \lambda = 300, a = 0.2, b = 0.4.$

5 $l = 3,\ \lambda = 600, a = 0.4, b = 0.7.$

6 A light elastic string of modulus 30 N and natural length 1 m hangs unstretched. Find the work done by a man in stretching the string a distance of 0.1 m. How much extra work is needed to extend the string by a further 0.3 m?

7 An elastic string of natural length 1 m and modulus 50 N is horizontal and has one end fixed and is stretched by applying a force of 5 N to the other. Find the work done by this force.

2.4 Kinetic energy and the work-energy principle

The word energy occurs very often in everyday life and there are many different forms of energy e.g. heat energy, electrical energy, chemical energy. The use of the word is often very loose but in any scientific work it is necessary to be a little more precise.

The energy of a particle is its capability to do work. This is not a particularly clear definition but one which you may understand a little bit more clearly by considering one particular form of energy encountered in Mechanics. This is **Kinetic Energy (K.E.)**, which, for a particle of mass m moving with speed v, is defined as $\frac{1}{2}mv^2$.

Kinetic energy is effectively the energy possessed by a particle by virtue of its motion. The unit of kinetic energy is the joule (J).

The kinetic energy can be related to the capacity of a particle to do work by imagining a particle of mass m set off with speed v on a rough horizontal floor. The friction force will act in the opposite direction to the motion and reduce speed. The point of application of the force of friction moves and therefore the force does work until the particle comes to rest. Therefore the moving body had some capacity to do work.

This can be made more precise by assuming that the friction force F is constant so that the retardation of the particle is $\frac{F}{m}$. Denoting the distance that the particle has moved by s and applying $v^2 = u^2 + 2as$ with $v = 0$, $u = v$ and $a = -\frac{F}{m}$ gives

$$0 = v^2 - 2\frac{F}{m}s,$$

and therefore $Fs = \frac{1}{2}mv^2$. Therefore the work done in reducing the speed to zero is equal to the particle's original kinetic energy. This should make clearer the idea of energy as a capability to do work.

The above result relating the work done to a change in kinetic energy is a simple example of a general result proved in 2.7 which is known as the **work-energy principle** and which states that

Change in K.E = Total work done by the forces acting.

This general principle can be used to solve many mechanical problems very simply. A particular advantage of using it is that there are some forces which do no work and they do not have to be considered at all. The simplest example of such forces is the reaction of a smooth surface, if a particle moves along such a surface then the reaction has no component in the direction of motion and therefore does no work. Another example is the tension in a taut light string.

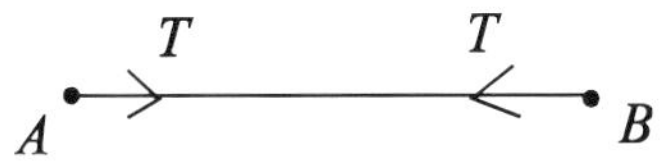

The tension act away from the ends as shown in the diagram, and if A moves a distance d then so does B and therefore the total work done is zero. This is still true if the string passes over a smooth pulley.

Another advantage of using the work-energy principle is that, even if the precise nature of the forces acting is not known, it can be used to find the total work done, provided the change in kinetic energy is known.

Many problems involving motion under constant forces can often be solved just as easily by using the constant acceleration formulae and it often is just a matter of preference which method you use. In examinations you may however be told something like "using energy considerations find ... ", and then you would have to use the work-energy principle.

The principle of conservation of mechanical energy described in 2.5 is a very slight variant of the work-energy principle and in many circumstances is effectively identical to it.

Example 2.5

A particle is dropped from rest at a height of 3 m above a horizontal floor, find the speed with which it hits the floor.

The mass of the particle is not given and it will therefore be denoted by m kg.
If the speed with which the particle hits the floor is v ms^{-1} then the change in its kinetic energy is $\frac{1}{2}mv^2$ J. The force of gravity is acting in the direction of motion so the work done by it is $3 \times 9.8\,m$ J = $29.4\,m$ J. Equating these gives $v^2 = 58.8$ and $v = 7.67$.
This problem can also be solved by using the constant acceleration formulae.
The downwards acceleration is 9.8 ms^{-1} and substituting $a = 9.8$, $s = 3$, $u = 0$ in $v^2 = u^2 + 2as$ gives the same answer.

Example 2.6

A particle of mass 0.3 kg, dropped from a height of 4 m reaches a speed of 8 ms^{-1} just as it hits the floor. Find the work done by air resistance.

The change in kinetic energy is $\frac{1}{2} \times 0.3 \times 64$ J = 9.6 J.

The work done by gravity is $0.3 \times 4 \times 9.8$ J = 11.76 J.
The work-energy principle then gives

$$9.6 = 11.76 + \text{work done by air resistance},$$

the work done by the air resistance is therefore –2.16 J, the minus sign showing that the resistance is acting in the opposite direction to the motion.

Example 2.7

A particle of mass 0.3 kg moves on a smooth horizontal plane under the action of a horizontal force of magnitude 12 N. Find the speed of the particle after it has moved a distance of 5 m from rest.
The reaction of the plane does no work and neither does the force of gravity since it also is perpendicular to the motion. (These forces need not have to be considered separately since, as mentioned in 5.1 of M1 book, forces perpendicular to the line of motion are in equilibrium. Therefore the nett force is zero and therefore so is the work done).
The work done during the motion is therefore 12×5 J = 60 J. This is equal to the change in kinetic energy, i.e. $\frac{1}{2}0.3 \times v^2$ J, where the final speed is v ms^{-1}. This gives

$$v = \sqrt{400} = 20..$$

The acceleration along the plane of the particle is $\frac{12}{0.3}$ ms^{-2} = 40 ms^{-2} and again using $v^2 = u^2 + 2as$ with this value of a gives the same result.

Example 2.8

A heavy parcel of mass 10 kg is pushed along a rough horizontal floor by a force and its speed increases from 1 ms^{-1} to 2 ms^{-1} whilst it travels a distance of 5 m. Given that the coefficient of friction is 0.5, find the work done by the pushing force.
Find also this force for the two cases
(i) when it is assumed to be constant,
(ii) when it is assumed to be of the form kx where x is the distance moved from the point where the speed is 1 ms^{-1}.

(i) The change in kinetic energy is $5 \times (2^2 - 1^2)$ J = 15 J. The reaction is 98 N and therefore the force of friction is 49 N. The force of friction acts in the opposite direction to the motion and therefore the work done by it is -49×5 J = -245 J.
The work done by gravity and by the normal reaction are, as in Example 2.7, zero.
Therefore the work-energy principle gives

$$15 \text{ J} = \text{Work done by pushing force} - 245 \text{ J},$$

the work done by the pushing force is therefore 260 J.
If the pushing force is assumed to be F N, then the work done would be $5F$ J so $F = 52$.

(ii) If the force is assumed to be of the form kx N, where x m is the displacement from the point where the speed is 1 ms^{-1}, then the work done is $\int_0^5 kx\,dx$ J = 12.5 kJ.

This gives $k = 20.8$.

Example 2.9

A particle of mass 0.3 kg moves along the x-axis under the action of an attractive force directed towards the origin and of magnitude $\frac{6}{x^2}$ N when the particle is at a distance of x m from the origin. It is projected in the positive x direction with a speed of 10 ms^{-1} from the point where $x = 1$. Find its speed for $x = 2$.

Denoting the speed when $x = 1$ by v ms^{-1}, the change in kinetic energy is $(0.15v^2 - 0.15 \times 100)$ J. The force is acting in the opposite direction to the motion so

the work done is $-\int_1^2 \frac{6}{x^2}\,dx$ J = $\left(\frac{6}{x}\right)_{x=1}^{x=2}$ J = -3 J.

The work energy principle gives

$$0.15v^2 - 15 = -3,$$

giving $$v = \sqrt{80} = 8.94.$$

Example 2.10

When the displacement from the origin of a particle of mass 0.4 kg is x m, the component of force acting on it in the positive x direction is $(8 + 6e^{-x})$ N. Given that the particle has speed 2 ms^{-1} at the origin, find its speed when $x = 1$.

If the speed when the particle is at a distance of 1 m is denoted by v ms^{-1}, the change of kinetic energy is $(0.2v^2 - 0.2 \times 2^2)$ J $= (0.2v^2 - 0.8)$ J.
The motion is in the direction of the force and the work done moving from $x = 0$ to $x = 1$ is $\int_0^1 (8 + 6e^{-x})dx$ N. The work- energy principle gives

$$0.2v^2 - 0.8 = \int_0^1 (8 + 6e^{-x})dx\ ,$$

i.e. $$0.2v^2 = \int_0^1 (8 + 6e^{-x})dx + 0.8 = 14.8 - 6e^{-1} = 12.59,$$

giving $$v = 7.93 \text{ ms}^{-1}.$$

For problems where the forces acting are dependent only on position it is possible, from the work - energy principle, to derive the principle of conservation of mechanical energy. This is slightly simpler to apply in cases where all the forces are of a standard type.

Exercises 2.4

1 Find the kinetic energy of

(i) a particle of mass 0.2 kg moving with a speed of 8 ms^{-1},

(ii) a car of mass 800 kg moving at a speed of 22 ms^{-1},

(iii) a woman of mass 55 kg running at a speed of 4 ms^{-1}.

2 A car of mass 600 kg decreases its speed from 25 ms^{-1} to 20 ms^{-1}. Find the change in its kinetic energy.

3 A particle of mass 0.4 kg moving with speed 20 ms^{-1} has its kinetic energy suddenly reduced by 10 J. Find the new speed of the particle.

4 A bullet of mass 0.02 kg moving with speed 100 ms^{-1} enters a block of wood and comes to rest after moving a distance of 0.05 m. Find the resistance of the wood

(i) assuming that it is constant,

(ii) assuming that it is directly proportional to the distance the bullet has entered the wood.

5 When the brakes are applied, a car of mass 1000 kg comes to rest, from a speed of 12 ms^{-1}, in a distance of 40 m. Assuming that the other resistances acting on the car are of magnitude 90 N, find the work done by the braking force.

6 A car of mass 1000 kg is pushed by two men, one at each back corner. Each one exerts a force of 100 N at an angle of 15° to the direction of motion of the car and there is a constant resistance of magnitude 80 N acting. Find

(i) the work done by the men in moving the car a distance of 10 m,

(ii) the speed attained from rest in 10 m.

7 A boy of mass 30 kg slides a vertical height of 5 m from rest down a water chute. Find the speed he attains.

8 A man pushes a wheel barrow, of mass 35 kg, with a force of magnitude 20 N at an angle 30° to the horizontal. There is a resistance to motion of magnitude 10 N. Find, given that the wheel barrow is moved a distance of 10 m from rest,

(i) the work done by the man,

(ii) the speed attained.

9 A ball of mass 0.4 kg thrown vertically upwards with a speed of 10 ms^{-1} comes to instantaneous rest at a height of 4.5 m above the point of projection. Find the magnitude of the work done by the air resistance. Assuming that the magnitude of the work done by the air resistance is the same on the downwards path, find the speed with which the ball returns to the point of projection.

10 The speed of a particle of mass 0.15 kg sliding on a rough floor decreases from 7 ms^{-1} to 4 ms^{-1} while it moves a distance of 6 m. Find

(i) the work done by friction,

(ii) the coefficient of friction.

11 A particle of mass 0.4 kg is projected with speed 15 ms^{-1} up a rough plane inclined at an angle of 40° to the horizontal, the coefficient of friction being 0.3. Use the work-energy principle to find the distance that the particle moves up the plane before coming to rest.

12 A particle of mass 0.5 kg, free to move along the x-axis, is attracted towards the origin by a force $\frac{10}{x^3}$ N, when the particle is at a distance of x m from the origin. Given that it is projected from the point $x = 1$ with speed 10 ms^{-1} in the positive x direction, find its speed when $x = 2$.

13 A particle of mass 0.5 kg moves along the x-axis under the action of an attractive force directed towards the origin and of magnitude $\frac{10}{x^2}$ N when the particle is at a distance of x m from the origin. It is projected in the positive x direction with a speed of u ms^{-1} from the point where $x = 1$. Find the condition that u has to satisfy in order that the particle does not return to its initial position.

2.5 Potential energy and energy conservation

For forces, like those considered in 2.2, which depend only on position it is possible to define a second form of energy, **the potential energy**, which can be used to solve relatively complicated problems where more than one type of such force is involved. This approach is particularly useful where two or more standard type forces, such as gravity and the force in an elastic string, are involved.

Potential Energy (P.E.) can only be defined for forces which depend on position and is the work done against the force to move its point of application (usually a particle) from a standard position to its present position. Alternatively it can be regarded as the work done by the force in moving its point of application from its present position to a standard one. Potential energy is energy possessed by a particle by virtue of its position.

If the force in the positive x direction is $F(x)$, the work done against it in moving from the standard position $x = a$ to the position $x = x$ is

$$-\int_a^x F(s)\mathrm{d}s,$$

where the standard position (i.e. the position of zero potential energy) is $x = a$.

Potential energy due to gravity

For the force of gravity, the standard position is often taken to be ground level, but any appropriate level is satisfactory. If x is measured upwards then the force in the x direction acting on a particle of mass m is $-mg$, so the potential energy due to gravity (the gravitational potential energy) at height h above the zero level is mgh. Similarly, the potential energy at height H below the zero level is $-mgH$.

If a particle is released from rest at a height h above ground, it immediately starts moving i.e. work is being done. This again is consistent with energy being a capacity to do work. By the time the particle reaches the ground, its potential energy is zero but it will have gained kinetic energy.

In working out the gravitational potential energy of a particle you should remember that it is positive if the particle is above the zero level and negative if it is below this level.

Potential energy of an elastic string

For an elastic string, the zero of potential energy is the point where the string is just unstretched i.e. the extension s is zero. The work done against the tension in extending the string, moving from $s = 0$ to $s = x$, is $\displaystyle\int_0^x \frac{\lambda s}{l}\mathrm{d}s = \frac{\lambda x^2}{2l}$, where λ is the elastic modulus and l is the natural length. The potential energy of a stretched string, extended a distance x, is therefore $\displaystyle\int_0^x \frac{\lambda s}{l}\,ds = \frac{\lambda x^2}{2l}$.

This is sometimes called the elastic potential energy or the energy stored in the string. The same result holds for a spring compressed by a distance x.

The potential energy is effectively a method of calculating the work done by particular kinds of forces and the idea of potential energy can be used to state the work-energy principle in a slightly different way. The details are given in 2.7 where it is shown that

Total mechanical energy is constant provided all forces are dependent only on position,

where the total mechanical energy is the sum of the kinetic energy and the potential energy of all the forces acting.

This is the principle of conservation of mechanical energy, and forces which depend only on position are, for obvious reasons, called conservative forces.

Forces which do no work, like those normal to the direction of motion and the tension in a taut string, can be ignored in working out potential energy.

If there are non-conservative forces present, the principle of conservation of mechanical energy has to be replaced by

Change in total mechanical energy = Work done by non-conservative forces.

If a force is conservative, i.e. depends only on position, the work done in moving from $x = a$ to $x = b$ is $\int_a^b F(x)\mathrm{d}x$ and the work done in going back from $x = b$ to $x = a$ is $\int_b^a F(x)\mathrm{d}x = -\int_a^b F(x)\mathrm{d}x$. The total work done from $x = a$ to $x = b$ and back from $x = b$ to $x = a$ is therefore zero. Therefore another way of testing whether a force is conservative is to say that the total work from a point to another one and back is zero. This test can be used to show that frictional forces, which at first sight appear to be constant, are not conservative. If a particle slides on a rough horizontal plane, then there is a frictional force of magnitude μmg acting on the particle, where μ is the coefficient of friction. Moving directly from $x = 0$ to $x = a$, the work done by the force of friction is $-\mu mga$, since the motion is in the opposite direction to the force.

On moving back from $x = a$ to $x = 0$, a further amount of work $-\mu mga$ is done by the friction force since it is again acting in the opposite direction to the motion. Therefore a non-zero amount of work is done moving from a point and then back. Therefore frictional forces are not conservative.

The principle of conservation of mechanical energy can be used whenever the forces are conservative but it is most useful in problems involving springs or strings and the force of gravity, since the potential energies for these are known. Questions involving the use of conservation of energy will give information at various points of the motion and it is a good idea to set out a solution in a way which shows clearly the energies at these points and then apply the conservation of mechanical energy for all possible points.

Example 2.11

A particle of mass m is thrown vertically upwards with an initial speed u. Find (i) the greatest height reached, (ii) the speed when the particle is at a height h which is less than the greatest height.

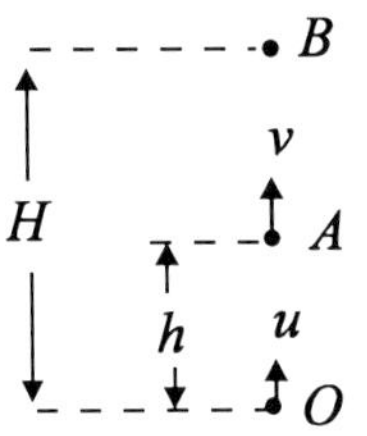

The points involved in the problem are the initial point O, the point A at height h and the point B of greatest height which will be taken to be at a height H. At this point the speed will be zero. The speed at A will be denoted by v.

At O, P.E. $= 0$, K.E. $= \frac{1}{2}mu^2$,

At A, P.E. $= mgh$, K.E. $= \frac{1}{2}mv^2$,

At B, P.E. $= mgH$, K.E. $= 0$.

Putting the total mechanical energy at O equal to that at B gives

$$\frac{1}{2}mu^2 = mgH,$$

so that $H = \dfrac{u^2}{2g}$. Equating the total mechanical energy at A to that at O gives

$$\frac{1}{2}mv^2 + mgh = \frac{1}{2}mu^2.$$

Solving for v gives $$v = \sqrt{u^2 - 2gh}.$$

This particular problem could have been solved just as simply by using the equations of motion under uniform acceleration.

Example 2.12

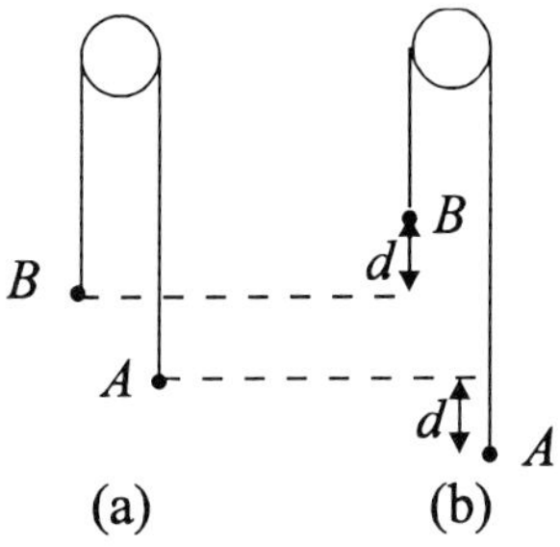

Diagram (a) shows two particles A and B of masses $5m$ and m attached one to each end of a light inextensible string passing over a smooth light pulley. Initially the particles are held at rest with the string taut and then released. Find, by using conservation of energy, the speed of A when it has dropped a distance d.

The total work done by the tension is zero and therefore, if both particles are considered, the total mechanical energy is conserved. Both particles also move with the same speed and if one drops a distance d the other rises by the same distance. The initial position and that when particle A has dropped a distance d are shown in diagrams (a) and (b).

Diagram (a) Particle A : K.E. = 0, P.E. = 0,

Particle B : K.E. = 0, P.E. = 0.

Diagram (b), Particle A : K.E. $= \frac{1}{2}\, 5mv^2$, P.E. $= -5mgd$,

Particle B : K.E. $= \frac{1}{2}\, mv^2$, P.E. $= mgd$.

Equating the total energy at both positions gives

$$3mv^2 - 4\,mgd = 0.$$

Therefore $$v = \sqrt{\frac{4gd}{3}}\,.$$

This example could have been solved as in 5.3 in the M1 book by finding the acceleration and using the constant acceleration formulae but, in this instance, the use of conservation of energy avoids the calculation of acceleration.

Example 2.13

A particle is released from rest at a point A on a smooth plane inclined at an angle of 30° to the horizontal. Find its speed when it has moved to a point B a distance of 8 m down the plane.

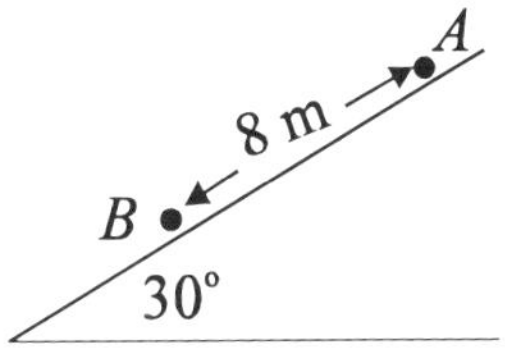

Apart from gravity, the only force acting on the particle is the reaction of the plane. This is perpendicular to the motion and does no work; therefore total mechanical energy is conserved.

The mass is not given so it will be denoted by m kg and the speed at B will be denoted by v ms^{-1}. At A the particle will be at a height of $8 \times \sin 30^\circ\ m = 4$ m above B.

At A : K.E. $= 0$, P.E. $= m9.8 \times 4$ J $= 39.2m$ J.

At B : K.E. $= \frac{1}{2}mv^2$ J, P.E. $= 0$.

Equating the total energies gives

$$39.2m = \frac{1}{2}mv^2,$$

so that $v^2 = 78.4$ and $v = 8.85$.

This problem could have been solved by finding the component along the plane of the force of gravity; this is $\frac{1}{2}mg$. The acceleration down the plane is therefore $\frac{1}{2}g$ and the constant acceleration formulae can be used.

Example 2.14

A particle of mass 0.4 kg is attached to one end of an elastic string of modulus 2 N and natural length 0.25 m. The other end of the spring is attached to a fixed point O on a smooth horizontal table. The string is extended a distance of 0.05 m and the particle then released from rest. Find

(i) the speed of the particle when the string returns to its unstretched position,

(ii) the speed when the extension is 0.02 m.

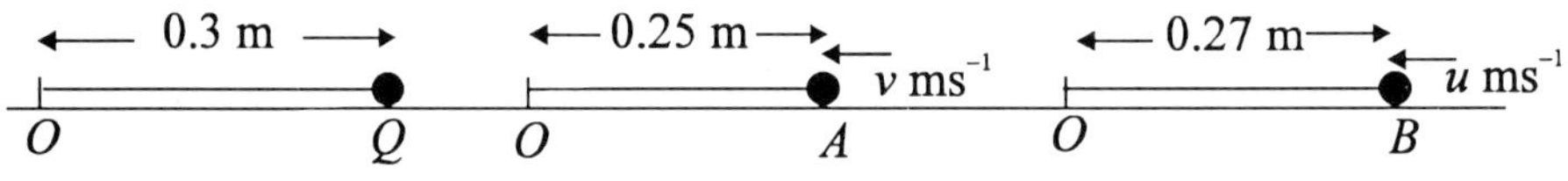

The diagrams show the initial position, when there is zero extension and when the extension is 0.02 m.

There are three points that have to be considered, the initial point Q, the point A of zero extension and the point B with extension 0.02 m. The velocities at A and B are denoted by v ms^{-1} and u ms^{-1}, respectively. The nett force perpendicular to the table is zero and therefore does no work.

The formula for the potential energy of an elastic string shows that when the string is extended by x m its potential energy is $\frac{\lambda x^2}{l} = \frac{2x^2}{2 \times 0.25}$ J $= 4x^2$ J.

At Q, P.E. $= 4 \times (0.05)^2 = 0.01$ J, K.E. $= 0$.

At A, P.E. $= 0$, K.E.$= \frac{1}{2} \times 0.4v^2 = 0.2v^2$ J,

At B, P.E. $= 4 \times (0.02)^2$ J, K.E.$= 0.2u^2$ J.

Equating the energy at Q to that at A gives

$$0.2\,v^2 = 0.01,$$

so $$v = 0.22.$$

Equating the energy at Q to that at B gives

$$0.2\,u^2 + 4\times(.02)^2 = 0.01,$$

so that $$u = 0.2.$$

Example 2.15

A particle of mass 0.6 kg is attached to one end of an elastic string of modulus 352.8 N and of natural length 0.5 m. The other end of the string is attached to a fixed point O. Initially the particle is held at O and released from rest.

Find the maximum extension of the string. This is a model of bungee jumping.

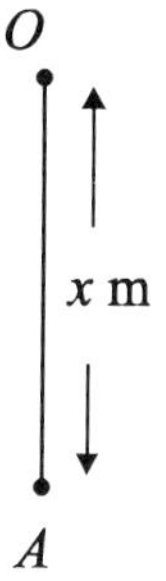

The two positions of the particle are shown in the diagram. It will drop until it comes to instantaneous rest at the point A at a distance x m below O, so the kinetic energy is zero at the start and the end of the motion.

There are two terms which contribute to the potential energy, the gravitational potential energy and the elastic potential energy. The formula for the potential energy of the elastic string shows that the elastic potential energy when the particle is at a depth of x m below O is $\dfrac{352.8(x-0.5)^2}{2\times 0.5}$ J provided $x > 0.5$, otherwise it is zero.

At O, Gravitational P.E. = 0,

Elastic P.E. = 0,

K.E. = 0.

At A, Gravitational P.E. = $-\,0.6\times 9.8\,x = -\,5.88x$ J,

Elastic P.E. = $\dfrac{352.8(x-0.5)^2}{2\times 0.5}$ J,

K.E. = 0.

Equating the total energy at O and A gives

$$\frac{352.8(x-0.5)^2}{2\times 0.5} - 5.88x = 0.$$

Expanding $(x - 0.5)^2$ and collecting the tems in the equation gives

$$352.8x^2 - 358.68x + 88.2 = 0.$$

This is a quadratic equation for x. Using the formula for solving the quadratic gives the roots as 0.6 and 0.417. The equation obtained is only valid when the elastic string is taut, i.e. $x > 0.5$, so the correct solution is $x = 0.6$.

Example 2.16

Find the speed of the particle in the above example when the particle is

(i) at a depth 0.3 m below O,

(ii) at a depth 0.55 m below O.

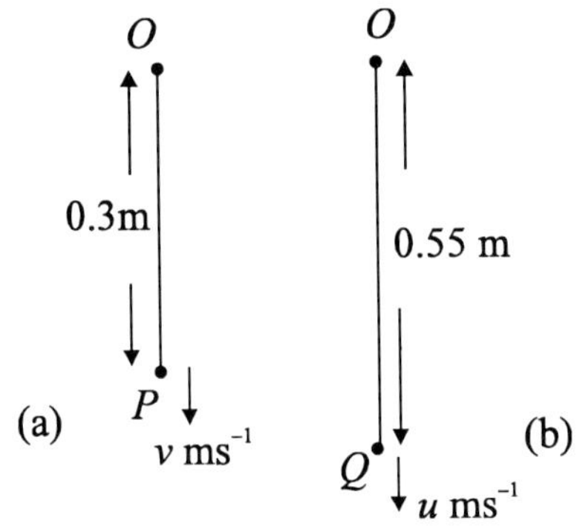

Diagram (a) shows the point P corresponding to the first case and diagram (b) shows the point Q corresponding to the second case. The velocities at P and Q are denoted by v ms^{-1} and u ms^{-1} respectively.

Case (i)

The string will be slack at P and therefore will have no elastic potential energy. The point O is taken to be the zero level of potential energy.

At O, Gravitational P.E. = 0,

Elastic P.E. = 0,

K.E. = 0.

At P, Gravitational P.E. = $-0.6 \times 9.8 \times 0.3$ J = -1.764 J,

Elastic P.E. = 0,

K.E. $= \frac{1}{2} \times 0.6\, v^2$ J $= 0.3v^2$ J.

Equating the total energies at O and P gives

$$0.3\, v^2 - 1.764 = 0,$$

so that

$$v = 2.42.$$

Case (ii)

At Q, Gravitational P.E. = $-0.6 \times 9.8 \times 0.55$ J = -3.234 J,

Elastic P.E. = $\dfrac{352.8(0.55 - 0.5)^2}{2 \times 0.5}$ J = 0.882 J,

$$\text{K.E.} = 0.3u^2 \cdot$$

Equating the total energies at O and Q gives

$$0.3u^2 - 3.234 + 0.882 = 0.$$

The solution of this is $u = 2.8.$

Example 2.17

A particle of mass 0.4 kg is attached to one end of an elastic string of natural length 1 m and modulus 19.6 N, the other end of the string being attached to a fixed point O. Initially the particle is in equilibrium with the string vertical. It is then pulled to a point A at a distance of 0.2 m below the equilibrium position and released from rest. Find

(i) the length of the string in the equilibrium position,

(ii) the speed of the particle when it is at a depth of 0.1 m below the equilibrium position,

(iii) the position of the particle when it next comes to rest.

The first step is to find the equilibrium point E. If the extension of the string is y m then

$$\frac{19.6y}{1} = 0.4 \times 9.8,$$

so that $y = 0.2$ and so the length of the string in the equilibrium position is 1.2 m.

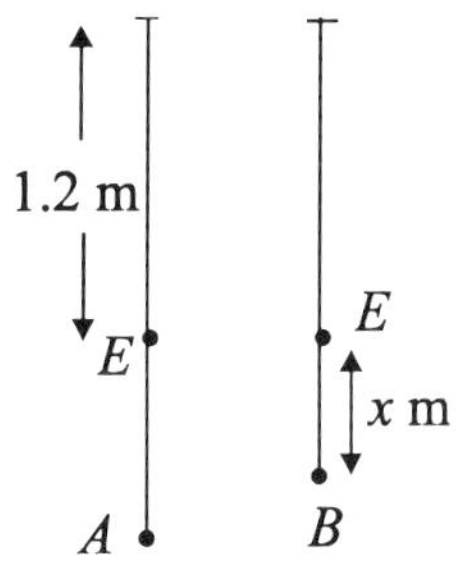

The diagram shows the initial point A of the particle and that when the particle is at a point B at a depth of x m below E. The extension in this position is $(0.2 + x)$ m and therefore the elastic potential energy is $\frac{19.6(0.2 + x)^2}{2}$. The initial elastic potential energy is found by substituting $x = 0.2$ in this. The zero of potential energy is taken at the equilibrium position.

At A, Gravitational P.E. $= -0.4 \times 9.8 \times 0.2$ J $= -0.784$ J

Elastic P.E. $= \frac{19.6(0.4)^2}{2}$ J $= 1.568$ J

K.E. $= 0$.

At B, Gravitational P.E. $= -0.4 \times 9.8x$ J $= -3.92x$ J

$$\text{Elastic P.E.} = \frac{19.6(0.2+x)^2}{2}\ \text{J}$$

$$\text{K.E.} = 0.2v^2\ \text{J.}$$

Equating the total energies at A and B gives

$$\frac{19.6(0.2+x)^2}{2} - 3.92x + 0.2v^2 = 1.568 - 0.784.$$

The equation simplifies to $9.8x^2 + 0.2v^2 = 0.392.$

Substituting $x = 0.1$ gives $v = 1.21$.

Substituting $v = 0$ gives $x = \pm 0.2$ so the particle next comes to rest at a height of 0.2 m above the equilibrium position where the string just becomes slack. Since this point is not an equilibrium point, the total force there is not zero and therefore it will move away from it. You can check that the force at this point is directed downwards so the particle will move down. It will stop instantaneously at the point A and the cycle then repeats itself.

Example 2.18

Answer (ii) and (iii) of Example 2.17 when the particle is pulled a distance of 0.3 m below the equilibrium point.

The only difference between this question and the previous one is that the initial position corresponds to $x = 0.3$. This means that the equation of energy is now

$$\frac{19.6(0.2+x)^2}{2} - 0.4\times 9.8\,x + 0.2v^2 = \frac{19.6(0.5)^2}{2} - 0.4\times 9.8\times 0.3.$$

Expanding $(0.2+x)^2$ and collecting terms gives

$$9.8x^2 + 0.2v^2 = 0.882.$$

Substituting $x = 0.1$ gives $v = 1.98$.

Substituting $v = 0$ gives $x = \pm 0.3$ so the particle next comes to rest at a height of 0.3 m above the equilibrium point. The string will however have become slack when the particle is at a distance of 0.2 m above the equilibrium position and therefore the above equation will only be valid for $x \le 0.2$. At this position $0.2v^2 = 0.49$.

From this position on, the only potential energy is that due to gravity and taking the zero of potential energy at this point gives, on applying conservation of energy $0.49 = 0.4 \times 9.8\,h$, where h denotes the height when the speed is zero and this is 0.125. So the height above the equilibrium position is 0.325 m.

Exercises 2.5

1 Find the change in potential energy in the following cases

(i) a particle of mass 0.3 kg moved upwards through a vertical distance of 1.5 m,

(ii) a man of mass 60 kg walking a distance of 50 m along and down a hill inclined at an angle of 45° to the horizontal,

(iii) a stone of mass 2 kg dropped a distance of 5 m from a bridge.

2 Find the increase in the gravitational potential energy of a man of mass 70 kg who climbs to the tenth floor of a block of flats. (Ground floor is floor 0). The distance between the floors is 3 m.

3 A stone is dropped from rest from a bridge to the water 10 m below, find the speed with which it hits the water.

4 A particle is projected with speed 5 ms^{-1} up a line of greatest slope of a smooth plane inclined at an angle of 40° to the horizontal. Use the principle of conservation of energy to find the distance the particle moves along the plane before coming to instantaneous rest.

5 Answer the previous question when the plane is rough with coefficient of friction 0.2.

6 A particle of mass m rests on a smooth horizontal table and is connected by a light inextensible string, passing over a smooth pulley, to a particle of mass $3m$. The particles are held at rest with the string taut and then released. Find, by using conservation of energy, the speed of the particles when the heavier one has dropped a distance h.

7 Two particles of masses 0.8 kg and 0.6 kg are connected by a light inextensible string passing over a small smooth pulley. They are released from rest with the string taut. Find their speeds when the heavier particle has dropped a distance of 0.2 m.

8

The diagram shows a spring, with one end fixed, in a horizontal tube. The spring is of natural length 0.2 m and elastic modulus 160 N. A particle of mass 0.02 kg is placed on the free end and the spring compressed a distance of 0.05 m and then released. Find the speed of the particle when the spring is at its unstretched position.

9 Two particles each of mass m are connected by a light elastic string of natural length a and modulus 4 mg. The string lies on a smooth horizontal table and is stretched by equal forces until it is of length $1.6a$. Both particles are then released simultaneously. Assuming that both particles move with the same speed, find the value of the speed when they are a distance a apart.

In questions 10 to 12, one end of a light elastic string, of modulus kmg N and natural length l m, is fixed at a point O and a particle of mass m kg is attached to the other end. The particle is then released from O. Find the extension of the string when the particle first comes to instantaneous rest.

10 $k = 1$, $l = 1$. 2.15

11 $k = 4,\ l = 3.$

12 $k = 5,\ l = 2$.

In questions 13 to 14, one end of a light elastic string, of modulus kmg N and natural length l m, is fixed at a point O and a particle of mass m kg is attached to the other end. The particle is initially at rest in equilibrium and is then pulled down a distance d m and released from rest. Find the distance below O of the point where the particle first comes to instantaneous rest.

13 $l = 3,\ k = 6,\ d = 0.5.$

14 $l = 2,\ k = 8,\ d = 0.4.$

2.6 Power

A machine, in practice, is required not only to do a certain amount of work but to do that work in a limited interval of time. A powerful car shows its power by accelerating rapidly i.e. it produces kinetic energy more rapidly than a car of lesser power.

Power is the rate at which work is done. If 1 joule is produced in 1 second, the rate of working is 1 watt. The watt (W) and the kilowatt (kW = 10^3 W) are the standard units of power.

If the point of application of a force F moves a small distance δx in a small time interval δt then the change in work, denoted by δW, is $F\,\delta x$. The rate of doing work is found by dividing δW by δt and letting δt become very small. Therefore the rate of working, i.e. the power, is the value of $F\dfrac{\delta x}{\delta t}$ as both δx and δt become very small. This, from the idea of a derivative as a rate of change, is $F\dfrac{\mathrm{d}x}{\mathrm{d}t}$ and, from the definition of velocity, is Fv.

When working out problems for moving vehicles, the rate of working of the engine of a vehicle can be calculated from analysing its motion.

It is then assumed that all this power is transmitted without loss to the driving wheels.

If the work done between some standard time and time t is denoted by $W(t)$, since it could vary with time, then the definition of power P gives

$$P = \frac{\mathrm{d}W}{\mathrm{d}t}.$$

Since W depends on t, then so will P and therefore the work done between $t = 0$ and $t = T$ is found by integrating this i.e.

$$\text{Work done} = \int_0^T P\,\mathrm{d}t\,.$$

For a constant power, but only then,

Work done over a time interval T is PT.

The relation between power and work can be used to work out the power necessary for a pump to bring water up through a height h and then pump it out at speed v, as in the diagram.

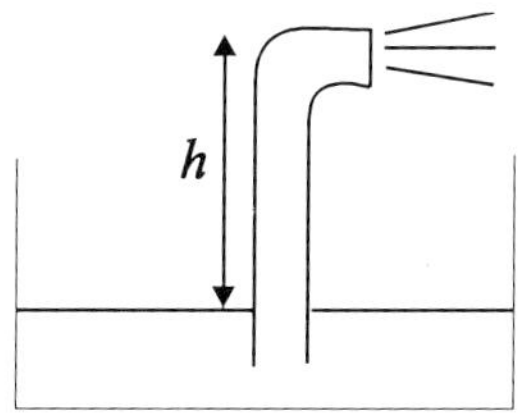

The work done by the pump is converted into the kinetic and potential energy of the water and the amount of work done per second is therefore $\frac{1}{2}mv^2 + mgh$, where m denotes the mass per second lifted. Since the power P is assumed to be constant, this work is equal to P and therefore

$$P = \frac{1}{2}mv^2 + mgh.$$

Example 2.19

The force acting on a particle of mass 0.2 kg and moving along a straight line is such that, at time t s, the velocity of the particle is t^4 ms^{-1}. Find the rate at which the force acting on the particle is working.

The first step is to find the force, this is 0.2 × acceleration. The acceleration can be found by differentiating the velocity and is $4t^3$ ms^{-2}. Therefore the rate of working is

$$0.8\,t^3 \times \text{velocity} = 0.8\,t^7 \text{ W}.$$

Example 2.20

The rate of working at time t s, of the force acting on a particle 0.4 kg moving on a straight line is $6t^5$ W. Given that the particle has speed 2 ms^{-1} at time $t = 0$, find its speed at time $t = 1$.

The change in kinetic energy is the work done, and the work done between $t = 0$ and $t = 1$ is

$$\int_0^1 6t^5 dt \text{ J} = 1 \text{ J}.$$

If the speed when $t = 1$ is v ms^{-1}, then the change of kinetic energy is $0.2v^2 - 0.8$ J. Therefore $v^2 = 9$ and $v = 3$.

Example 2.21

A pump is required to raise 100 kg of water a second, through a height of 15 m and discharge it through a nozzle with speed 10 ms^{-1}. Find the minimum rating of pump required if the pump is

(i) 100% efficient,

(ii) 50 % efficient.

The change in P.E. per second is $100 \times 9.8 \times 15$ J $= 14700$ J.

The change in K.E. per second is 50×10^2 J $= 5000$ J.

The total change in energy per second, i.e. the work done per second is 19 700 J. Therefore the minimum rate of working, if the pump is 100% efficient, is 19.7 kW. For 50% efficiency, the rate would have to be 39.4 kW.

2.7 Derivation of basic results

In this section, a derivation of the work-energy principle will be given for the case of a particle of mass m, moving along the x-axis, under the action of a force whose component in the positive x direction is denoted by F. The velocity in the positive x direction at time t will be denoted by v.

Newton's second law of motion gives

$$m\frac{\mathrm{d}v}{\mathrm{d}t} = F.$$

Multiplying this equation by v gives

$$mv\frac{\mathrm{d}v}{\mathrm{d}t} = Fv.$$

The left hand side can be written, on using the product rule for differentiation, as $\frac{\mathrm{d}}{\mathrm{d}t}\left(\frac{1}{2}mv^2\right)$ which is the rate of change of kinetic energy. The right hand side is the power, i.e. the rate of doing work. The equation is therefore

Rate of change of kinetic energy = Rate of doing work.

Therefore integrating this gives

Change of kinetic energy over any interval = Work done over the interval.

This is the work-energy principle in its simplest form. The proof is effectively for a particle moving on a line and the work done is that done by forces along the line. It also holds when the work done by forces not along the line is included, this is because the work done by the components of these force perpendicular to the line will be zero, since the motion of these components will be perpendicular to the line.

If the only forces acting are dependent on position, then introducing the potential energy produces the principle of conservation of mechanical energy. This can be shown as follows.

The work done by a force F in moving from $x = x_1$ to $x = x_2$ is $\int_{x_1}^{x_2} F(x)\,dx$. This can be rewritten from the properties of integrals as

$$\int_a^{x_2} F(x)\,dx - \int_a^{x_1} F(x)\,dx.$$

The potential energy at $x = x_1$, for example, is, $-\int_a^{x_1} F(x)\,dx$, therefore the above expression for the work done is equal to

$$-\text{P.E. at } x = x_2 + \text{P.E. at } x = x_1.$$

The work energy principle can therefore be rewritten as

$$(\text{K.E. at } x = x_2 - \text{K.E. at } x = x_1) = -(\text{P.E. at } x = x_2 + \text{P.E. at } x = x_1).$$

This can again be rearranged as

$$(\text{K.E. at } x = x_2 + \text{P.E. at } x = x_2) = (\text{K.E. at } x = x_1 + \text{P.E. at } x = x_1).$$

The sum of the Kinetic and potential energy is the total mechanical energy and therefore

Total Mechanical energy is constant provided all forces are dependent only on position.

Potential energy can only be defined for conservative forces. If there are non-conservative forces present, then the work done by all the forces is $-$ change in P.E. of the conservative forces + work done by the non-conservative forces. The principle of conservation of mechanical energy has then to be replaced by

Change in total mechanical energy = Work done by non-conservative forces.

Exercises 2.6

1 A particle is of mass 0.5 kg and the component of its velocity in the positive x direction at time t s is $4 \exp 3t$ ms^{-1}. Find the rate at which the force acting on it is working.

2 Find the total work done in 10s by a force when the rate of working is

(i) 3 kW

(ii) $3\left(1 - \exp\left(-\dfrac{t}{10}\right)\right)$ kW.

3 A particle of mass 0.8 kg has speed 4ms^{-1} at time $t = 0$s and the force acting on it is working at a rate of $10t^9$ W at time ts. Find its speed when $t = 2$.

4 A water pump is to raise 50 kg of water a second through a height of 20m. The water emerges as a jet with speed $50 ms^{-1}$. Find the kinetic energy and the potential energy given to the water each second and hence find the power that the pump would have to develop if

(i) it were 100% efficient,

(ii) it were 75% efficient.

5 A pump delivers 220 kg of water per minute, the water being delivered in a horizontal jet at a speed of $30 ms^{-1}$. Find the kinetic energy of the water delivered each second. The efficiency of the engine driving the pump is 35%. Find the rate at which this engine is working.

2.8 Problems involving vehicle motion

The problems already encountered involving vehicle motion have been such that the driving force has been given explicitly. This is not what happens in practice since what is normally known for a vehicle engine is its rate of working or power.
For cars, the old fashion unit of power, which is often referred to, is horse power (H.P.) and 1 H.P. = 745.7 watt. If an engine is working at P watts and the point of contact of the wheels with the ground is moving at speed v ms^{-1}, then the driving force F N at the wheels satisfies the equation

$$P = Fv.$$

This can be used to work out the driving force for vehicles working at a rate of P W moving with speed v ms^{-1}. (When a car is not skidding, the speed of the point of contact of the wheels is equal to that of the car, and this will normally be assumed).
Problems where the power developed by a vehicle is given are very similar to previous problems involving vehicle motion except that the force has to be worked out from the power and speed. Some problems require finding the steady speed at which a vehicle can travel when the engine is working at a given power. Since the vehicle is moving at a steady speed, the acceleration is given, it is in fact zero.
Sometimes the maximum speed may be given. A maximum is a stationary point, so

$\frac{dv}{dt} = 0$, i.e. the acceleration will be zero.

Example 2.22

A particular motor cycle develops a maximum power of 24 kW and, when working at this rate, its speed is 40 ms^{-1}. Find the driving force.

The driving force F N is such that

$$24000 = 40F,$$

giving F as 600.

Example 2.23

A car travels at constant speed, with its engine working at a rate of 40 kW, against a resistance of 1600 N. Find the speed.

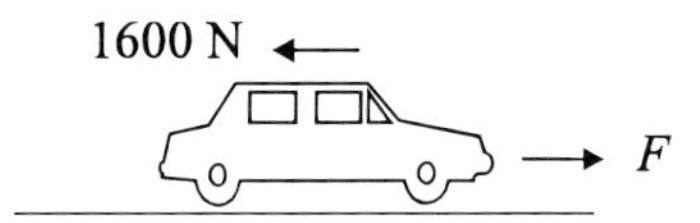

The forces acting are shown in the diagram. If v ms^{-1} denotes the speed of the car then $F = \dfrac{40\,000}{v}$ N. Since the acceleration is zero, the force is equal to the resistance i.e.

$$\frac{40000}{v} = 1600,$$

so that $v = 25$.

Example 2.24

The engine of a lorry of total mass 2 tonnes is working at 50 kW. The lorry is travelling at a constant speed of 20 ms^{-1}, along a level road. Find the total resistance to the motion.

If the power is increased to 60 kW, find the acceleration of the lorry at the instant it is moving with speed 20 ms^{-1} assuming that the resistances to motion remain constant.

When the power is 50 kW, the driving force F N is given by

$$F \times 20 = 50\,000,$$

so that $F = 2500$ N.

Since the lorry is moving at constant speed, the acceleration must be zero, i.e. the total force is zero so the resistance is 2500 N.

When the power is 60 kW, the driving force F N at the instant the speed is 20 ms^{-1} is

$$\frac{60\,000}{20}\text{ N} = 3000\text{ N}.$$

The total force on the lorry is (3000 – 2500) N = 500 N, the equation of motion is

$$2000a = 500,$$

where a ms^{-2} is the acceleration, therefore $a = 0.25$.

Example 2.25

A car of mass 1000 kg has a maximum speed of 35 ms^{-1} on a level road against a resistance of 400 N. Find, assuming the engine works at the same rate and that the resistance is unchanged, its maximum speed up a hill inclined at an angle α to the horizontal where $\sin\alpha = \frac{1}{7}$.

In this case the power is not given and will be assumed to be P W, the driving force is $\frac{P}{35}$ N and, since at maximum speed the acceleration, and hence the total force, is zero

$$\frac{P}{35} = 400.$$

Therefore $P = 14\,000$.

The forces acting on the car when moving at speed v ms^{-1} up the hill are shown in the diagram.

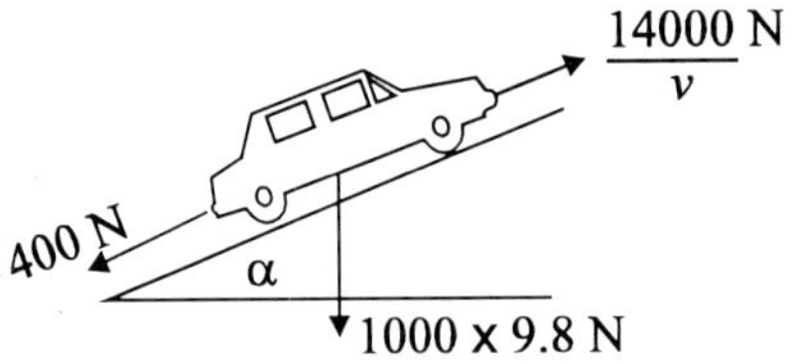

The total component of the force in N acting in the sense up the hill is

$$\frac{14000}{v} - 400 - 1000 \times 9.8 \times \sin\alpha = \frac{14000}{v} - 1800.$$

When the speed is a maximum the total force is zero i.e.

$$v = \frac{14000}{1800} = 7.8.$$

Exercises 2.7

1 Find the power developed when a force of 1500 N pulls a cart at a constant speed of 6 ms^{-1}.

2 Find the power that is developed by the engine of a car moving at a speed of 12 ms^{-1}, given that the driving force is 750 N.

3 A car, whose engine is working at a rate of 5 kW, is moving with speed 10 ms^{-1}, find the driving force.

4 A car travels along a horizontal road against a resistance of 600 N. Given that the engine is working at a constant rate of 4.8 kW, find the maximum speed of the car.

5 A car of mass 1000 kg moves on a horizontal road against a resistance of 600 N with the engine working at a rate of 8 kW. Find the acceleration of the car at the instant it is moving with a speed of 10 ms^{-1}.

6 A car of mass 1200 kg travelling along a horizontal road, with its engine working at a constant rate, against a resistance of 500 N, has a maximum speed of 25 ms^{-1}. Find the rate at which the engine is working.
Find also the maximum speed with which the car can climb a hill inclined at an angle α to the horizontal, where $\sin\alpha = \frac{1}{14}$, assuming that the resistances and the rate of working of the engine are unchanged.

7 A train of mass 300 tonnes travels along a straight level track. The resistance to motion is 18 kN. Find the tractive force required to produce an acceleration of 0.1 ms^{-2}, and the power in kW which is then developed by the engine when the speed of the train is 10 ms^{-1}.
Find also the maximum speed attainable when the engine is working at a rate of 360 kW.

8 A car of mass 1500 kg travels up a slope of inclination α to the horizontal, where $\sin\alpha = \frac{1}{49}$, against constant frictional resistances of 3600 N. Find the maximum speed of the car given that the engine works at a rate of 80 kW. After reaching the top of the slope the power is switched off and the car descends a slope of inclination β to the horizontal against the same constant frictional resistances at constant speed. Calculate $\sin\beta$.

9 A car of mass 1000 kg has a maximum speed of 15 ms^{-1}, against a constant frictional force equal to one eighth of the weight of the car, up a slope inclined at an angle α to the horizontal where $\sin\alpha = \frac{1}{7}$. Find the maximum speed of the car on a horizontal road assuming that the engine works at the same rate.
If the car descends the same slope with its engine working at half this rate, find the acceleration of the car at the moment when its speed is 25 ms^{-1}.

10 The resistive forces opposing the motion of a train of total mass 50 tonnes are 5000 N.

(a) Find the power necessary to keep the train moving along a straight level track at a constant speed of 10 ms^{-1}.

(b) If this power is suddenly increased by 10 kW when the train is moving along the level track at 10 ms^{-1}, find the initial acceleration of the train.

(c) When the train climbs a hill, of inclination α to the horizontal, at a constant speed of 8 ms^{-1}, the engine of the train is working at a rate of 180 kW. Find the value of $\sin\alpha$.

11 A car of mass 1600 kg climbs a slope of inclination α to the horizontal, where $\sin\alpha = \frac{1}{14}$, at a steady speed of 12 ms^{-1}. Given that the frictional resistance is 400 N, calculate the power, in kW, developed by the car.

When the car reaches the top of the slope, the power is switched off and the car descends a slope of inclination β to the horizontal, where $\sin\beta = \frac{1}{28}$. Assuming that the frictional resistance remains at 400N, calculate the acceleration with which the car descends this slope.

12 A car of mass 1600 kg is moving along a horizontal road. The resistance to the motion of the car is 800 N. Calculate the acceleration of the car at the instant when its speed is 7.5 ms^{-1} and its engine is working at 15 kW.

13 When the car is moving with speed v ms^{-1} the resistance to its motion is $(200 + 2.5v)$N. Find the maximum speed of the car when its engine is working at a rate of 5 kW.

Miscellaneous Exercises 2

1 A particle is thrown vertically upwards with a speed of 5 ms^{-1} from a point 2 m above the ground. Find

(a) the greatest height above the ground reached,

(b) the speed of the particle when it hits the ground.

2 A girl throws a ball vertically upwards so that its initial speed is 10 ms^{-1}.

(a) Draw a diagram showing the forces acting on the stone and state clearly the cause of each force.

(b) Find the maximum height that the ball would reach if the only force acting were that due to gravity and which may be assumed to be constant.

(c) It turns out that the ball, which has a mass of 0.2 kg, only reaches a height of 4.5 m; find the work done by the resistance as the ball travels from the girl's hand to its maximum height.

3 A boy of mass 60 kg starting with a speed of 1 ms^{-1} slides down a chute in a swimming pool and strikes the water at a speed of 9 ms^{-1}. Find the work done against friction if the chute is 5 m high.

If the length of the slide is 20 m find the frictional force, assuming it to be uniform.

4 A toboggan run is straight, 1213 m long and drops 157 m from start to finish. One day a toboggan and its rider with a combined mass of 112 kg, starting from rest, achieved a speed of 117 kmh^{-1} at the finish.

(a) Calculate the gain in kinetic energy.

(b) Find the loss in potential energy.

(c) Determine the work done against resistive forces assumed constant.

5 A vehicle of mass 4000 kg is moving up a hill inclined at an angle α to the horizontal where $\sin\alpha = \frac{1}{20}$. Its initial speed is 2 ms^{-1}. Five seconds later it has travelled 15 m up the hill and its speed is then 6 ms^{-1}. Find the change in the kinetic energy and potential energy of the vehicle.

Given that the engine is working at a constant rate of 44 kW, find the total work done against the resistive forces (which may not be assumed to be constant) during this five second period.

6 An elastic spring which obeys Hooke's law has natural length 0.5 m. When the extension is 0.05 m the tension in the spring is 50 N. Find the work done when the spring is extended from a length of 0.6 m to a length of 0.7 m.

7 The gravitational force per unit mass at a distance r ($> R$) from the centre of the earth is $\dfrac{gR^2}{r^2}$, where R is the radius of the earth and g is the acceleration due to gravity on the earth's surface. Find the work done in moving a particle of mass m from $r = 2R$ to $r = 3R$.

Find the speed when $r = 3R$ of a particle whose speed when $r = 2R$ was $\sqrt{\dfrac{gR}{2}}$.

8 A catapult consists of two lengths of elastic, each of modulus 20 N and natural length 0.2 m. The catapult is stretched so that the length of each elastic is increased by 0.08 m.

Ignoring the effect of gravity and using energy considerations, find the speed that the catapult will give to a stone of mass 0.02 kg.

9 The end A of a light elastic string AB of natural length 1.2 m is fixed. When a particle of mass 2.4 kg is attached to the string at B and hangs freely under gravity, the extension of the string is 0.09 m. Find the modulus of elasticity of the string.

The particle is now pulled vertically a further 0.12 m and released from rest. By energy considerations, find the greatest height above the point of release in the subsequent motion.

10 A particle P of mass 0.02 kg is attached to one end of a light elastic spring of natural length 0.5 m and modulus 1.6 N, the other end of which is attached to a fixed point A on a smooth horizontal table. The particle is released from rest on the table when the spring is straight and its extension is 0.25 m. Find the speed of the particle

(i) when the spring is at its natural length,

(ii) when the spring is compressed by 0.10 m.

11 A particle of mass 2 kg is attached to two elastic strings, each of natural length 0.5 m and modulus 15 N, the other ends of the strings being attached to two fixed points A and B which are at a distance of 1 m apart in the same horizontal line. The particle is dropped from rest from the midpoint of AB.

(a) Show that the tension T N in each string is given by $T = 15(\sec\theta - 1)$, where θ denotes the angle between each string and the horizontal.

(b) Find, correct to two decimal places, the acceleration of the particle when $\theta = 60^\circ$.

(c) Using energy considerations find, correct to two decimal places, the speed of the particle when $\theta = 60^\circ$.

12 A particle is suspended from a fixed point O by a light elastic string which is of natural length a and hangs in equilibrium at a distance $\frac{5a}{4}$ below O. Given that the particle is released from rest at O, find the distance it falls before it first comes to rest.

13 One end O of a light elastic string of natural length $4l$ is attached to a fixed point. A particle P of mass m is attached to the other end P of the string and the string hangs in equilibrium with $OP = 5l$. The particle is pulled down vertically a further distance $\frac{l}{2}$ and released from rest. Show that P rises a distance l before first coming to instantaneous rest.

14 Find also, for the configuration in the previous question, the maximum height to which P would rise if it had been released from rest at a depth of $2l$ below the equilibrium position.

15 One end of a light elastic string of modulus 4.9 N and natural length 0.5 m is attached to a fixed point A and a particle of mass 0.1 kg is attached to the other end. The particle is held at A and released from rest. Its speed when it has dropped a distance of x m is v ms^{-1}.

(i) Write down an expression for its speed when $x \le 0.5$.

(ii) Show by use of energy that, for $x \ge 0.5$, $v^2 = 117.6\ x - 9.8x^2 - 24.5$.

16 In the dangerous sport of bungee diving an individual attaches one end of an elastic rope to a fixed point on a river bridge. He/she is then attached to the other end and jumps over the bridge so as to fall vertically downwards towards the water. The rope should be such that the diver comes to rest just above the surface of the water. In order to find which particular ropes are suitable, experiments are carried out with weights, rather than people, attached to the rope. In one experiment it was found that when a weight of mass m was attached to a particular rope of natural length a and dropped from a bridge at a height $3a$ above the water level, then the weight just reached the level of the water. Show that the modulus of elasticity of the rope is $\frac{3mg}{2}$.

The weight of mass m is removed and a weight of mass $\frac{5m}{2}$ is then attached to this rope and dropped from the same height. Find the speed of the weight just as it reaches the water.

When the weight emerges from the water, its speed has been reduced to zero by the resistance of the water. Show, by using conservation of energy, and assuming that the rope does not slacken, that the subsequent speed v of the weight at height h above the water level is given by

$$v^2 = \frac{gh}{5a}(2a - 3h).$$

Describe the subsequent motion of the weight.

17 A particle of mass m is attached to one end of an elastic string of modulus 4 mg and natural length a, the other end of the string being attached to a fixed point O.

The particle is released from a point at a distance $\frac{5a}{3}$ directly below O.

Find (i) the height to which the particle will rise,

(ii) the speed of the particle when it is at a distance of $\frac{3a}{2}$ below O.

18 A water pump raises 40 kg of water a second through a height of 20m and ejects it with a speed of 45 ms^{-1}. Find the kinetic energy and potential energy per second given to the water and the effective rate at which the pump is working.

19 A car of mass 1000 kg, whose engine is working at a rate of P watts, moves at a constant speed of 20 ms^{-1} on a horizontal road. Find, in terms of P, the total frictional resistance on the car.

The car then freewheels (i.e. without the engine exerting any force) down a hill inclined at an angle α to the horizontal, where $\sin\alpha = \frac{1}{14}$, at constant speed.

Find P.

Assuming the same frictional resistance and that the engine is working at the rate of P watts, find the numerical value of the acceleration of the car at the instant it is moving uphill with speed 7 ms^{-1}.

20 A car of mass 1000 kg moves, with its engine working at its maximum rate, at a constant speed of 10 ms^{-1} up a hill inclined at an angle α to the horizontal, where $\sin\alpha = \frac{1}{14}$. The functional resistance to motion is R N. Express the maximum rate of working in terms of R.

With the engine still working at its maximum rate, the car descends the hill at a constant speed of 20 ms^{-1}. Given that the frictional resistance is now 4R N, find the value of R.

21 A locomotive of mass M kg working at a rate of R kW ascends a straight track which is inclined at angle α to the horizontal. When the speed is v ms^{-1}, the acceleration is a ms^{-2}. Find an expression for the resistance at speed v ms^{-1}.

22 A car of mass 1500 kg is moving along a horizontal road. The resistance to the motion of the car is 750 N. Assuming that the car's engine works at 15 kW find

(i) the maximum constant speed at which the car can travel,

(ii) the acceleration of the car when its speed is 8 ms^{-1}.

23 A car of mass 1300 kg tows a trailer of mass m kg along a level road. The resistance on the car is 1000 N and that on the trailer is 1.5m N. Find the total power developed by the engine when $m = 600$ and the car and trailer are moving at a steady speed of 20 ms^{-1}. For $m = 1700$ and the car moving at a speed of 25 ms^{-1} and its engine working at a steady rate of 75 kW, find

(i) the acceleration of the car and trailer,

(ii) the tension in the coupling between the car and trailer.

State whether or not the car can maintain a steady speed of 25 ms^{-1} with the engine working at a steady rate of 25 kW.

Given that the safest minimum speed for travel on a motorway is 18 ms^{-1} and that the car engine is working at a rate of 72 kW, find the range of possible values of m so that the car and trailer can travel at steady speeds which are no lower than the safest minimum speed.

24 A car travels at a constant speed of 20 ms^{-1} on a horizontal road against constant resistance of 1000N. Find the rate of working of the engine.

The car is then attached to a caravan by a towbar and the resistance to the motion of the caravan is 800 N. Given that the rate of working of the engine is 35 kW, find the maximum speed of the car and caravan on a horizontal road and obtain the tension in the tow bar.

The total mass of the car and the caravan is 1.8 tonnes and the car pulls the caravan directly up a hill which is inclined at an angle α to the horizontal, where $\sin\alpha = \frac{1}{35}$. Given that the car is working at a rate of 42 kW, calculate the acceleration up the hill when the car and caravan are travelling at 14 ms^{-1}. The non-gravitational resistances to the motion of the car and the caravan may be assumed constant.

25 The maximum speed of a car, whose engine can develop 15 kW, on a level road is 30 ms^{-1}. Find the total resistance to the motion of the car at its maximum speed. Given that the non-gravitational resistance to the motion of the car varies as the square of the speed and that the mass of the car is 800 kg, determine the power developed by the engine when the car moves at a constant speed of 35 ms^{-1} directly up a hill which is inclined at an angle α to the horizontal where $\alpha = \dfrac{1}{21}$.

26 A car of mass 800 kg is moving at a constant speed of 50 ms^{-1} on a level road. The non gravitational resistance to the motion of the car at all speeds and on all roads is 700 N. Calculate the rate at which the engine of the car is working.

When the car climbs directly up a certain hill, it has a maximum speed of 25 ms^{-1} and the engine is working at a rate of 20 kW. Calculate the angle of inclination of the road to the horizontal.

Find the acceleration of this car when travelling at 25 ms^{-1} up a hill inclined at an angle α to the horizontal, where $\sin\alpha = \dfrac{1}{21}$, with its engine working at the rate of 15 kW.

27 A car of mass 800 kg is pulling a trailer of mass 200 kg up a hill inclined at an angle α to the horizontal, where $\sin\alpha = \dfrac{1}{14}$. When the total force exerted by the engine is 1000N, the car and trailer move up the hill at a steady speed. Find the total frictional resistance to the motion of the car and trailer.

When the car and trailer are travelling at a steady speed of 10 ms^{-1} up the hill, the power exerted by the engine is instantaneously increased by 2 kW.

Find

(i) the instantaneous acceleration,

(ii) the instantaneous tension in the coupling between the car and trailer, given that the total resistance on the trailer is 75 N.

Chapter 3

Impulse and Momentum

After this chapter you should

- be able to apply the impulse momentum principle to forces which are dependent on time,
- know what is meant by impulsive tension,
- be able to solve problems where bodies are connected together by inelastic strings.

3.1 Impulse-momentum Principle

In M1 6.1, we have seen that, for a constant force P acting on a particle of mass m for a time T, such that the velocity of the particle in the direction of the force changes from u to v, then

$$P.T. = m\,(v - u),$$

that is, impulse = change in momentum.

It is very unlikely that the force will be constant throughout contact and therefore a generalisation of the definition of impulse is necessary. As in the case of work, the generalisation can be seen from a graphical interpretation of impulse. Both the following diagrams show the behaviour of the component of force in a given direction with time t.

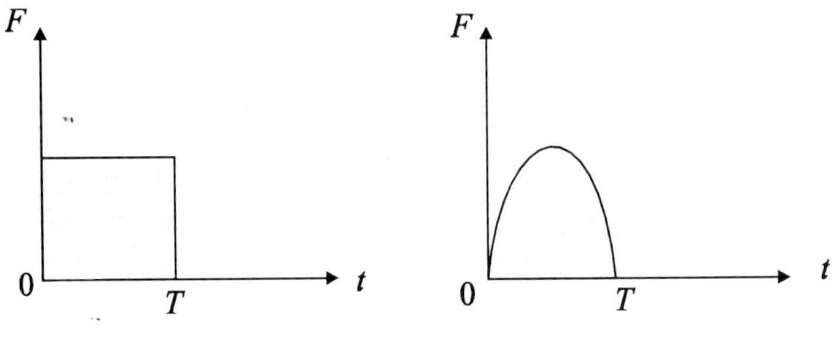

The left hand diagram shows the component to have a constant value whilst the right hand one shows variation with time; this is more likely to be a realistic form for a sharp blow since it vanishes at $t = 0$, and $t = T$. The impulse of the constant force is therefore the shaded area under the line and this suggests that the impulse is defined as $\int_0^T F \, dt$. The next step is to see whether this can enable a change of velocity to be found simply in terms of the impulse.

Newton's Law of motion gives

$$F = m\frac{dv}{dt}.$$

Integrating this equation from $t = 0$ to $t = T$ gives

$$\int_0^T F \, dt = \int_{t=0}^{t=T} m\frac{dv}{dt}$$

$$= [mv]_{t=0}^{t=T}$$

$$= (mv)_{t=T} - (mv)_{t=o}.$$

The right hand side of this equation is the change in momentum, the left hand side is the impulse acting and therefore the impulse-momentum principle holds for all forces.

Example 3.1

A ball of mass 0.3 kg is moving with speed 5 ms^{-1} just as it hits a horizontal floor and bounces off the floor, with a speed of 2 ms^{-1}. Find the impulse exerted on the ball by the floor given that the time of contact is 0.05s.

Taking the reference direction as upwards.

The momentum of the ball immediately after impact is $0.3 \times 2 = 0.6$ Ns upwards, and immediately before impact, it is $0.3 \times (-5) = -1.5$ Ns. The total change of momentum is $0.6 - (-1.5) = 2.1$ Ns.

The total force acting is $(F - 0.3 \times 9.8)$ N, where F N is the force exerted by the floor.

The total impulse is $\int_0^{0.05} (F - 0.3 \times 9.8)dt$ Ns

$$= \int_0^{0.05} F dt - 0.147 \text{ Ns}$$

Total impulse = change in momentum

$$\int_0^{0.05} F dt = 0.147 \qquad = 2.1$$

$$\int_0^{0.05} F dt \qquad = 2.247 \text{ Ns}$$

Exercises 3.1

1 A tennis ball of mass 0.08 kg moving horizontally towards the racquet with speed 6 ms^{-1} is hit by the racquet and leaves the racquet horizontally with a speed of 12 ms^{-1}. The ball and racquet are in contact for 0.04 s. Find the force acting assuming

(i) that it is constant,

(ii) that it is of the form ct N, where t is the time, in seconds, measured from impact and c is a constant.

2 A cricket ball of mass 0.15 kg moving horizontally with speed 14 ms^{-1} just as it reaches a batsman, is hit straight back horizontally with a speed of 24 ms^{-1}. The bat and the ball are in contact for 0.05 s. Find the form of the force exerted by the bat on the ball assuming that it can be expressed as $kt(0.05 - t)$ N, where k is a constant.

3 A ball of mass 0.2 kg falls vertically and when moving with speed 6 ms^{-1} is struck by a bat which is moving vertically upwards so that after the ball leaves the bat, it has a speed of 4 ms^{-1} vertically upwards. Find, assuming that the bat and ball are in contact for 0.05 s, the impulse exerted by the bat.

3.2 Impulsive Tensions

Strings

When a string jerks, equal and opposite tensions act suddenly at each end. So equal and opposite impulses act on the objects which are attached to each end of the string. If one end of the string is fixed, the impulse which act at the fixed end has no effect on motion. The object attached to the free end will undergo a change in momentum equal to the impulsive tension along the string. The momentum in the direction perpendicular to the string will remain unchanged.

Example 3.2

A light intextensible string of length $2l$ is fixed at one end to a point 0 on a smooth horizontal floor. A particle P of mass m kg is attached to the other end of the string. P is initially at a point A a distance l from 0. P is projected horizontally with speed u ms^{-1} at right angles to OA. Find the velocity of P immediately after the string becomes taut and the magnitude of the impulsive tension.

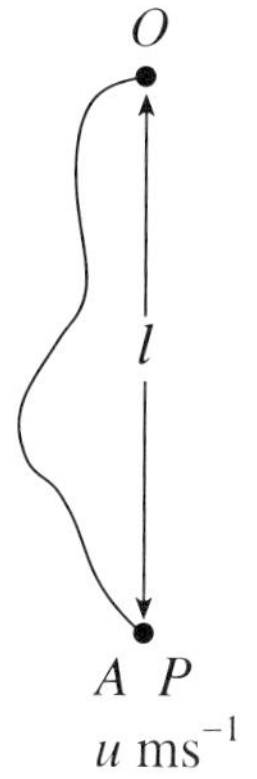

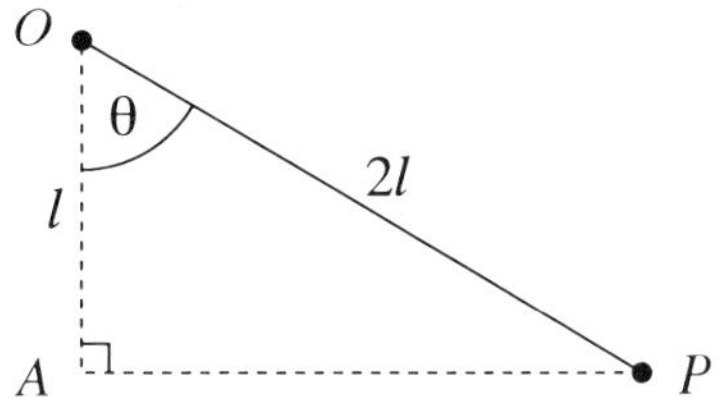

At the instant the string becomes taught, $OP = 2l$, $OA = l$ and $O\hat{A}P = 90^\circ$.

So $\cos \hat{A}OP = \frac{l}{2l} = \frac{1}{2}$ and $A\hat{O}P = 60^\circ$. Just before the jerk, P has velocity $u \cos 60^\circ$ perpendicular to the string and $u \sin 60^\circ$ in the direction of the string. After the jerk, P can no longer travel in the direction of the string which is now taut and P has velocity component v perpendicular to the string.

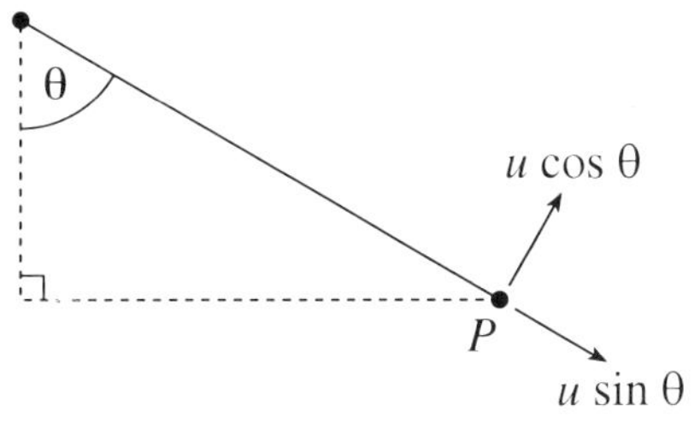

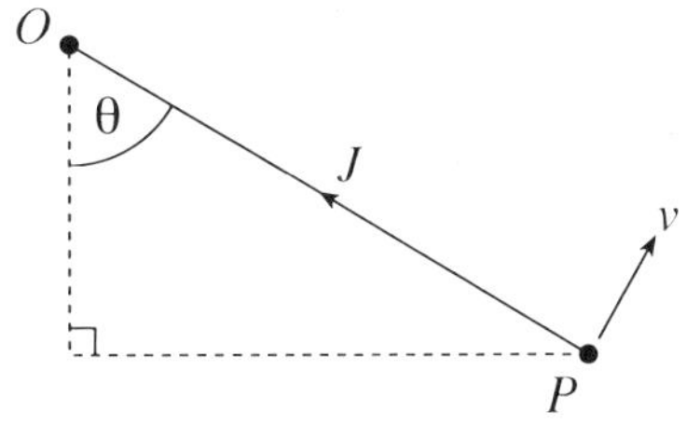

	Impulse	=	change in momentum
Along OP	J	=	$0 - (-mu \sin \theta)$
		=	$\frac{mu\sqrt{3}}{2}$

Perpendicular to OP

$$0 = mv - mu \cos 60^\circ$$

$$v = \frac{u}{2}.$$

3.3 Impulsive motion of connected particles

Particles moving along the same line

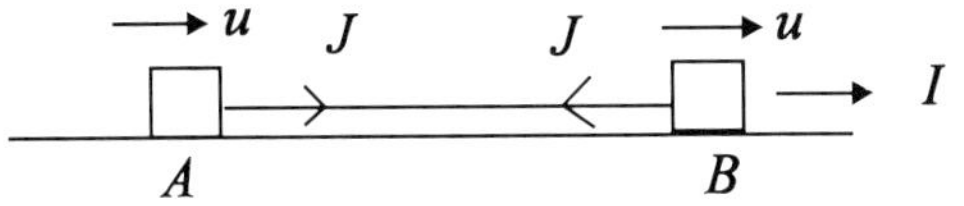

The typical problem is as shown in the diagram, two particles A and B, of mass m and M, respectively, are connected together by a light inextensible string and, when the string is taught, an impulse I is applied to B in the direction from A to B. Both particles will move with the same speed u as shown and therefore there will be an impulse J acting at A in the direction A to B. By Newton's third law, there will be an impulse of equal magnitude acting at B from B to A. This impulse which is acting along the string is usually called the impulsive tension even though it is not a force.

The total applied impulse is I and this, by the impulse momentum principle for a system of particles, is equal to the total change in momentum i.e. $(m + M)u$. Therefore

$$u = \frac{I}{m+M}.$$

The impulsive tension can now be found by applying the impulse momentum principle to particle A, i.e. $mu = J$, so that

$$J = \frac{mI}{m+M}$$

An alternative method would have been to apply the impulse momentum to both A and B. The equation obtained for B would be $I - J = Mu$. Eliminating J gives u as before. It is simpler for problems of this type, as for problems involving the motion of two particles, to consider the whole system first and then one of the particles.

Some care has to be used in considering the impulsive motion of connected particles. The diagram shows the two particles A and B discussed above moving with speed u in the direction AB when an impulse of magnitude I is applied to B in the sense from A to B.

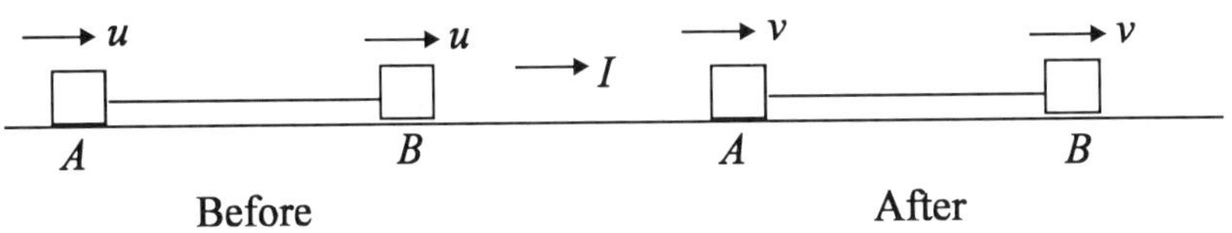

After the impulse has been applied they will both be moving with a new speed v and the impulse momentum principle for a system of particles gives

$$(m + M)(v - u) = I.$$

Therefore v can be found.

If the impulse had been applied from B to A and it had been assumed that both particles still moved together, then this would have given that they would both be moving to the left with speed v where

$$(m + M)(v + u) = I.$$

This would mean that there would be an impulsive tension to the left on the particle A. This is impossible and therefore in this case the impulse would only affect the particle B.

Example 3.3

Car A in the diagram is about to tow car B. The tow rope is slightly slack so that car A can reach a speed of 2.5 ms^{-1} before the rope tightens. Determine the motion of the cars immediately after the rope tightens. The masses of cars A and B are 1500 kg and 1250 kg respectively.

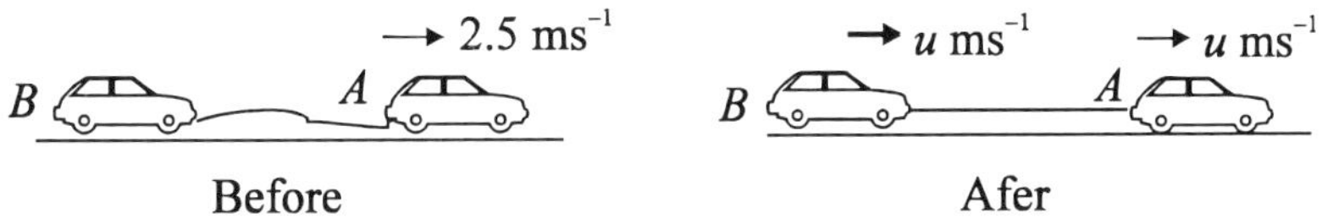

Immediately after the rope tightens the cars will be moving at the same speed of u ms^{-1}. In this case there is no applied impulse and the principle of conservation of momentum may be applied .

The principle of conservation of momentum gives

$$1500 \times 2.5 = (1500 + 1250)u$$

so that $u = 1.36$. The impulsive tension in the rope is $1250u$ Ns = 1700 Ns.

Example 3.4

Two particles A and B of mass $2m$ and $6m$ lie in a straight line, joined by an inextensible string, which is just taut. An impulse of magnitude $16mU$ is applied to B in the sense from A to B. Determine the subsequent motion.

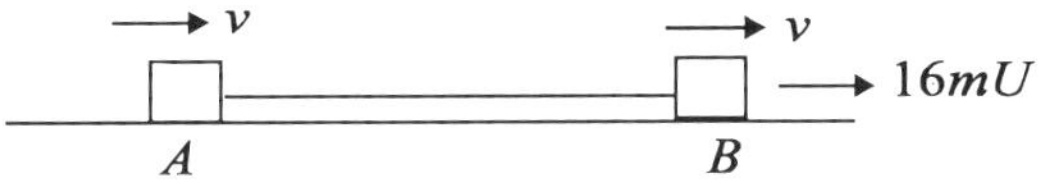

The only possible motion will be along the string and since the string is inextensible both particles move with the same speed v. The total momentum after the particles start moving is $2mv + 6mv = 8\,mv$. The impulse momentum principle gives

$$8mv = 16mU,$$

so that $$v = 2U.$$

The impulsive tension acts on A towards B and is denoted by I.

Applying the impulse momentum principle to A gives $I = 2mv = 4mU$.

If the original impulse had been from B to A, then there would have been no impulsive tension in the string, so A would not move and $6mv = 16mU$, giving

$$v = \frac{8U}{3}.$$

Problems involving pulleys

Problems involving particles on a string passing over a pulley can be solved by considering the system as a whole, as for the case of general motion involving pulleys, but it is not really a safe approach. It is better to apply the impulse momentum principle carefully to each particle. The most commonly occurring types of problems are illustrated in the following examples.

Example 3.5

Two particles of mass 0.4 kg and 0.6 kg attached one at each end of an inextensible string passing over a smooth pulley, as shown in the diagram, are set in motion. At the instant when the particles have a common speed of 3 ms^{-1}, the heavier particle hits a horizontal surface off which it does not rebound. (The surface is referred to as being inelastic.) Find the speed with which the heavier particle is first jerked into motion.

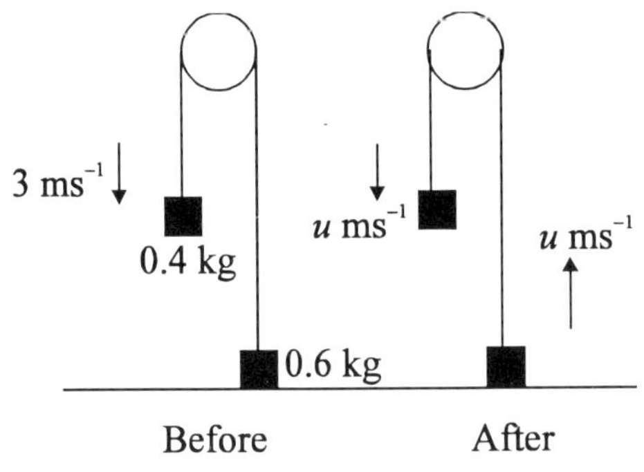

Once the heavier particle has stopped the lighter one continues upwards under gravity to its highest point and then falls, reaching the point where the string is about to become taut with speed 3 ms^{-1}. When the string becomes taut there will be an impulsive tension T Ns in the string and the heavier particle will jerk off the plane and both particles will start to move with a common speed u ms^{-1}.

Applying the impulse momentum principle to the heavier particle gives $T = 0.6u$.

The impulsive tension acting on the lighter particle will be upwards, the velocity of the particle will have changed from 3 ms^{-1} downwards to u ms^{-1} downwards. Therefore the change in linear momentum downwards is $0.4(u - 3)$ and this is equal to $-T$. Eliminating T gives

$$0.4(u - 3) + 0.6u = 0$$

i.e $$0.4u + 0.6u = 1.2$$

so that the heavier particle is jerked off with speed 1.2 ms^{-1}.

The equation for u is exactly the same as if the two particles had been in a straight line and the principle of conservation of momentum applied. That method should not be used to solve a problem in an examination as it needs careful justification but it could help as a check.

Example 3.6

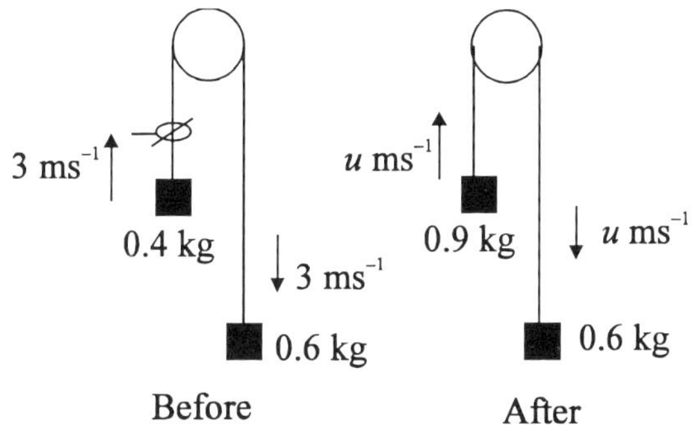

When the particles are moving freely with a speed of 3 ms^{-1} as shown in the diagram, the lighter particle picks up a mass 0.5 kg which is lying on a fixed ring through which the particle passes. Find the common speed of the system immediately after the mass has been picked up.

The particles move with a new unknown speed u ms^{-1}.

There will be an impulsive tension T in the string and this is the impulse acting on the combined particle so, applying the impulse momentum principle to this combined particle, $T = (0.5 + 0.4)u - 3 \times 0.4$. The velocity of the heavier particle, downwards, will change from 3 ms^{-1} to u ms^{-1} so the change in its linear momentum downwards is $0.6u - 0.6 \times 3$ and this is equal to $-T$. Eliminating T gives

$$(0.5 + 0.4)u - 0.4 \times 3 + 0.6u - 0.6 \times 3 = 0$$

i.e. $$(0.5 + 0.4)u + 0.6u = 0.4 \times 3 + 0.6 \times 3,$$

and $$u = 2.$$

Exercises 3.2

1 Two particles P and Q of mass 4 kg and 3 kg, respectively, lie on a smooth table connected together by a light inextensible string. Particle P is projected away from Q with speed 8 ms^{-1}. Find the common speed of the particles after the string becomes taut and the impulsive tension in the string.

2 Particle A, of mass 0.2 kg, lies at rest on a smooth horizontal table and at a distance of 0.4 m from its edge. The surface of the table is at a height of 2 m above the floor. Particle A is joined by a light inelastic string of length 0.9 m to a second particle B of mass 0.4 kg. This particle is placed at the edge of the table and then pushed over the edge in such a way that the string is perpendicular to the edge of the table. Find the speed of A when it starts moving and also the impulsive tension in the string.

Questions 3 to 6 refer to two particles A and B, of masses m kg and M kg respectively, connected by a light inextensible string passing over a light smooth pulley.

3 $m = 0.3$, $M = 0.2$, the system is set off from rest and, when both particles are moving with speed 2 ms^{-1}, the particle B picks up from rest an additional particle of mass 0.3 kg. Find the further distance moved before the system first comes to instantaneous rest.

4 $m = 0.5$, $M = 0.3$, the system is set off from rest and, after descending 5 m, the particle A strikes an inelastic floor and comes to rest. Find the time that it remains on the floor and the speed with which it is jerked off.

5 $m = 0.8$, $M = 0.4$, when both masses are moving with speed 2 ms^{-1} A passes through a small ring and a mass of 0.5 kg is removed from it. Find the time that elapses before A next passes through the ring.

6 $m = 0.5$, $M = 0.2$, the system is at rest with A resting on a smooth plane. A falling particle of mass 0.2 kg moving with speed 4 ms^{-1} strikes B and sticks to it. Find the height to which A rises.

More Examples

Example 3.7

Particles P, Q, each of mass m kg, are attached, one to each end of a light inextensible string of length $2l$ m. The particles lie on a smooth horizontal floor. Initially P is at point A and Q is at point B, a distance l m from A. Q is projected across the floor with velocity u ms^{-1} perpendicular to AB. Find the velocity of the particles immediately after the jerk and the magnitude of the impulsive tensions.

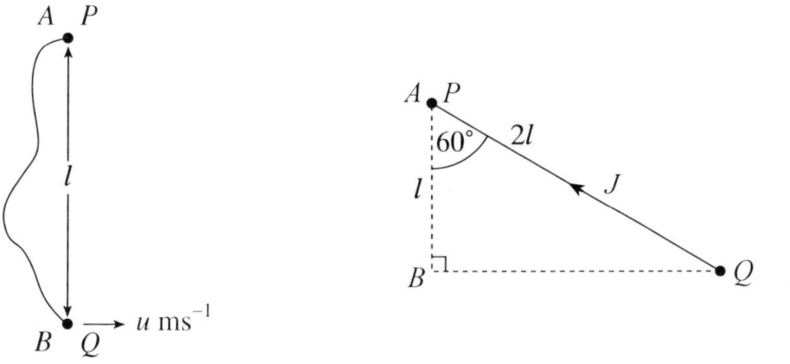

Just before the Jerk, P is at rest, Q has velocity $u \cos 60^{\circ}$ perpendicular to the string and $u \sin 60^{\circ}$ along the string.
Just after the Jerk, P, Q both move along direction of string with velocity v. Perpendicular to the string, there is no impulse on either particles and the velocities in this direction remain unchanged.

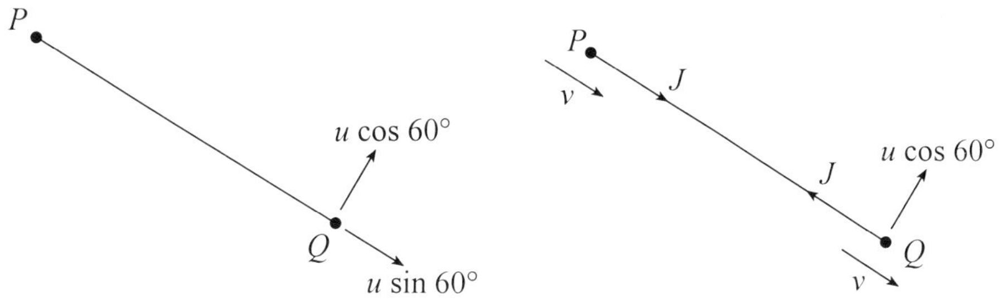

Impulse = change in momentum
Along the string

for P $\qquad J = mv$

for Q $\qquad -J = mv - \dfrac{mu\sqrt{3}}{2}$

Adding $\qquad 2v = \dfrac{u\sqrt{3}}{2}$

$$v = \frac{u\sqrt{3}}{4}.$$

Just after the Jerk,

velocity of P $= \dfrac{u\sqrt{3}}{4}$ ms^{-1} along string

$$\text{velocity of } Q = \sqrt{\left(\frac{u}{2}\right)^2 + \left(\frac{u\sqrt{3}}{4}\right)^2} = \frac{u\sqrt{7}}{4}\ \text{ms}^{-1}$$

in direction $\tan^{-1}\left(\frac{\left(\frac{u}{2}\right)}{u\sqrt{\frac{3}{4}}}\right)$ to the string

i.e. $\tan^{-1}\left(\frac{2}{\sqrt{3}}\right)$ to the string

Also

$$J = mv$$

$$= \frac{mu\sqrt{3}}{4}\ \text{Ns}$$

Example 3.8

A light inextensible string of length 2ℓ m carries masses P, Q, each of m kg one at each end and a mass R of $3m$ kg at its midpoint. P, Q and R are initially at rest on a smooth horizontal table at the corners of an equilateral triangle of side ℓ m. R is given a blow of impulse J along the perpendicular bisector of PQ. Find the velocities of the particles

(a) immediately after the blow,

(b) just before P and Q collide.

(a) Immediately after the blow, the velocities of P, Q and R are as shown in the diagram.

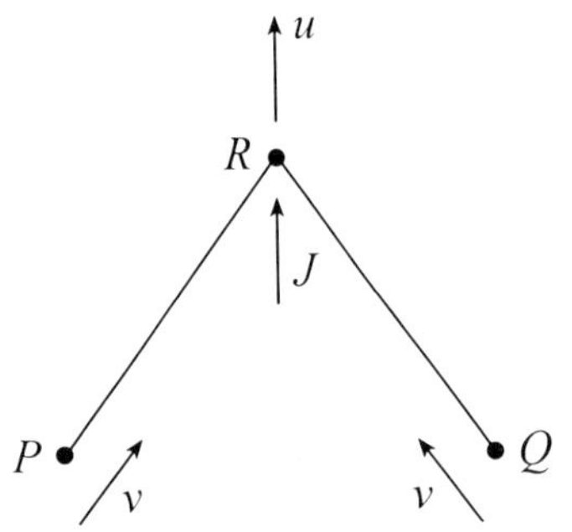

In direction of J

$$J = 3mu + mv\cos 30^\circ + mv\cos 30^\circ$$

$$= 3mu + mv\sqrt{3} \qquad \text{(i)}$$

Also, since the particles are connected, the velocities of the particles along the string at the two ends must be the same.

So for P and R, or for Q and R

$$v = u\cos 30^\circ = \frac{u\sqrt{3}}{2} \qquad \text{(ii)}$$

Solving these two equations gives $u = \dfrac{2J}{9m}$ and $v = \dfrac{J\sqrt{3}}{9m}$.

(b) Immediately before P and Q collide, their velocities are as shown in the diagram.

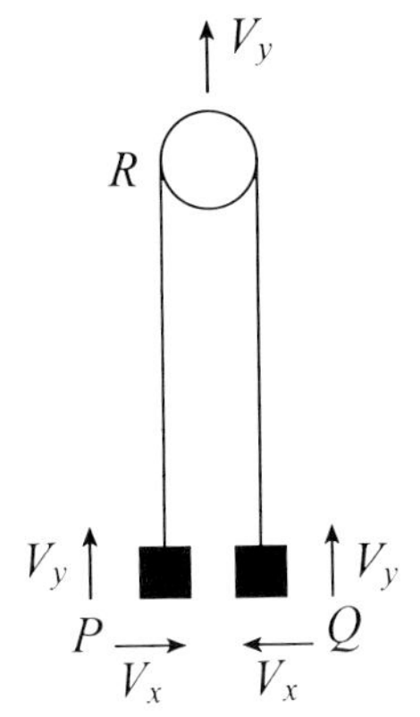

We now have

$$J = 3mVy + mVy + mVy$$

$$Vy = \frac{J}{5m}$$

which is the velocity of R.

In order to find Vx, it is necessary to remember that there is no change in K.E. immediately after the blow and just before P, Q collide.

Therefore, conservation of energy gives

$$\frac{1}{2}.3mu^2 + 2.\frac{1}{2}mv^2 = \frac{1}{2}.3m\ Vy^2 + 2.\frac{1}{2}m\left(V_x^2 + Vy^2\right)$$

Substituting for u, v and Vy, we obtain

$$Vx = \frac{J}{m\sqrt{90}} \quad \text{and} \quad \left(Vx^2 + Vy^2\right) = \frac{23J^2}{450m^2}.$$

Therefore P and Q have velocity with magnitude $\dfrac{J}{m}\sqrt{\dfrac{23}{450}}$ in a direction which makes an angle of $\tan^{-1}\left(\sqrt{\dfrac{5}{18}}\right)$ with the direction of the blow.

Exercises 3.3

1 Two particles P and Q, each of mass 5 kg, are connected by a light inextensible string of length 2m. Initially, they lie at rest on a smooth horizontal table with P at A and Q at B where A and B are a distance 1m apart. Particle Q is projected across the table with velocity 4ms^{-1} at a direction which makes an angle θ with AB. Find the speed of P when it begins to move, and the impulsive tension in the string when

(a) $\theta = 0$

(b) $\theta = 120^\circ$

(c) $\theta = 45^\circ$

(d) $\theta = 90^\circ$.

2 Two balls P and Q, of mass 4 kg and 2 kg respectively, lie on a smooth horizontal plane and are connected by a light inextensible string. Initially Q is due East of P. Q is given a blow such that, if it were free, it would move in a direction North-East with velocity 21 ms^{-1}. Show that Q actually moves with velocity 15.65 ms^{-1} in a direction North 72° East. Calculate the impulse applied to Q and the impulsive tension in the string.

3 Two particles of masses 4 kg and 3 kg are lying on a smooth table and are connected by a slack string. The first particle is projected along the table with a velocity of 21 ms^{-1} in a direction directly away from the second particle. Find the velocity of each particle after the string has become taut, and calculate the loss in kinetic energy.

The second particle is attached to a third particle of unknown mass by another slack string. After both strings have become taut, the common velocity of the particles is 10 ms^{-1}. Find the mass of the third particle.

4 Three small bodies of masses 0.4, 0.5 and 0.6 kg, respectively, lie in order in a straight line on a large smooth table, the distance between consecutive bodies being 0.15m. Two slack strings which are light and inextensible, each of length 0.6m, connect the first mass with the second and the second mass with the third. The third body is projected with speed 4.5 ms^{-1} directly away from the other two. Calculate the time which elapses before the first mass starts to move and the speed of the first mass when it starts to move. Calculate the loss in kinetic energy of the system.

Show that the ratio of the impulsive tensions in the two strings when the first mass is jerked into motion is 8 : 15.

Miscellaneous Exercises 3

1

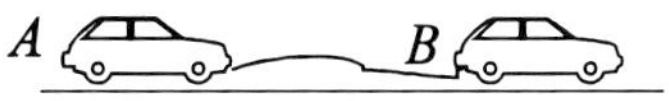

The diagram shows two cars A and B of masses 1200 kg and 1800 kg on a horizontal road. Car A has broken down and car B is about to tow it. The speed of B just as the tow rope tightens is 5 ms^{-1}. Modelling the cars as particles and assuming that the tow rope is light and parallel to the road along the line joining the cars, find

(i) the common speed of the two cars immediately after car A has started moving,

(ii) the impulsive tension in the tow rope.

The two cars then continue to move along the horizontal road until they reach a steady speed of 15 ms^{-1}. They then continue at this constant speed. Given that car B is working at a constant rate of 20 kW, find the total resistance acting on the two cars.

Given further that the resistance on each vehicle is proportional to its mass, find the tension in the tow rope.

2

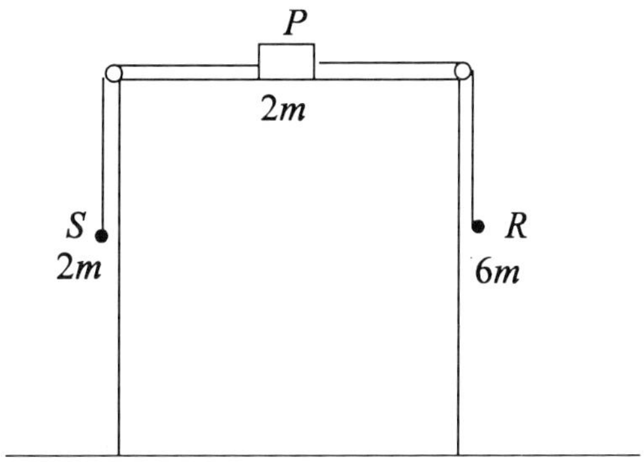

The diagram shows a particle P of mass 2m on a rough horizontal table and attached by light inextensible strings to particles R and S of mass $6m$ and $2m$ respectively. The coefficient of friction between P and the table is 0.5. The strings pass over light smooth pulleys on opposite sides of the table so that R and S can move freely with the strings perpendicular to the table edges. Given that the system is released from rest, find the magnitude of the common acceleration of the particles and the tension in the string joining P and S. After falling a distance d from rest, the particle R strikes an inelastic floor and is brought to rest. Find, for the period after R strikes the floor, the further distance that S rises. Find also assuming that in the subsequent motion P remains on the table and S never reaches the table, the speed at which R is jerked off the floor.

3. Two particles A and B each of mass m kg are connected by a light inextensible string of length 2ℓ, and rest on a smooth horizontal table at a distance ℓ apart. B is given a horizontal impulse mu Ns in a direction perpendicular to AB. Given that

(i) A is fixed

(ii) A is free to move,

find the impulse in the string on tightening and the velocity of B immediately afterwards. Show that the loss in kinetic energy in (i) is twice the loss in kinetic energy in (ii).

4. A smooth plane inclined at an angle of 30° to the horizontal is fixed such that its lower edge is at a height a m above a horizontal table. Two particles each of mass m kg are connected by a light inextensible string length of $2a$ m. Initially, P is held at the lower edge of the inclined plane and Q rest on the table vertically below P. P is then projected with velocity u ms^{-1} where $u > \sqrt{ga}$ upwards along the line of greatest slope of the plane.

(a) Find the impulsive tension in the string when Q is jerked into motion.

(b) Calculate the tension in the string while Q is moving.

(c) Given that Q just reaches the edge of the table, determine the value of u.

5 Two particles of masses 1 kg and 3 kg are connected by a light inelastic string of length 0.8 m. The string passes over a smooth peg. Initially the particles are held in contact with the peg. They are then dropped from rest at the same instant, one on each side of the peg.

(i) Find the speed of each particle immediately after the string tightens.

(ii) Calculate the loss in energy due to the sudden tightening of the string.

(iii) Find the time that elapsed from the time when the particles were dropped until the lighter particle reaches the peg again.

Chapter 4

Motion Under Gravity in 2 Dimensions

After working though this chapter you should

- be able, for motion in a plane, to find the magnitude and direction of velocity of a particle in two dimensions, given its component, and vice-versa.
- have a clear idea of the form of the path of a particle moving under gravity and be able to solve problems of a particle being projected from a point.

4.1 Basic kinematics

All the dynamical problems that you have come across so far have involved motion in a line where it is only possible to move backwards and forwards. The situation is not quite as simple for motion in a plane, for example, a ball moving on a horizontal plane can move in an infinite number of different directions. It is therefore necessary to generalise the idea of velocity to problems involving two dimensional motion. Velocity is defined to be something which completely represents the rate of change of position of a body, both the rate at which distance is covered and the direction in which the body is moving. It is not particularly easy at this stage, except for motion in a straight line, to give a clear definition of rate of covering distance though if you walk along any kind of curved path you are still aware of some kind of 'speed'. The basic point however is that velocity is something which has associated with it both a magnitude and a direction : its 'speed' and the direction of motion. The velocity of a man moving with constant speed 2 ms^{-1} at an angle θ North of East as in the left hand diagram is defined to be of magnitude 2 ms^{-1} at an angle θ North of East.

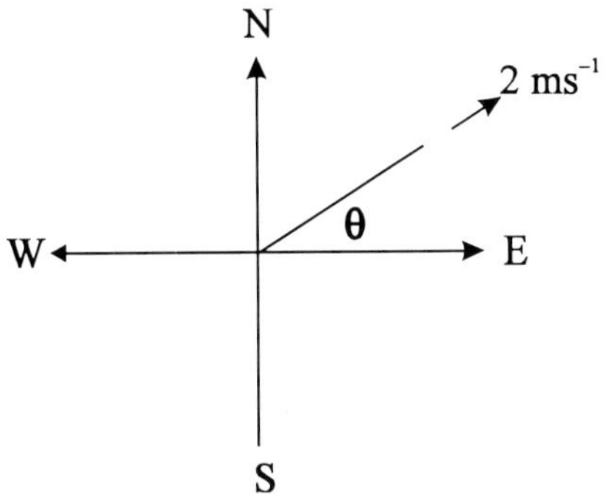

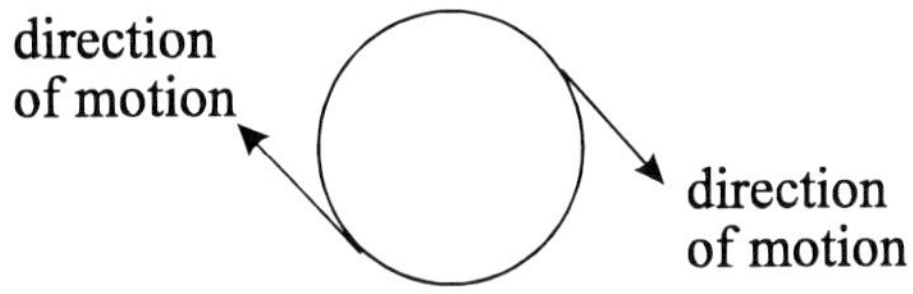

If the man were to walk round a circle as in the right hand diagram so that each small arc of the circle is described in equal time, then the direction of motion at a point would be along the tangent to the circle. His velocity at any point on the circle is then defined to be along the tangent to the circle at that point and its magnitude to be the circumference of the circle divided by the time to describe a complete circle. A more precise definition of this magnitude will be given later.

Therefore the velocity at a point can be represented by a line, the direction of the line representing the direction of motion and its length representing the magnitude. Velocity is therefore, like force, a vector. This means that any velocity can be regarded as a combination of two, or more, separate motions or components. A simple example is the motion of rain when it is windy. If there is no wind the rain will fall vertically downwards but when it is windy it falls at an angle. This is because the actual velocity of the rain is a combination of the velocity due to falling under gravity and the wind velocity.

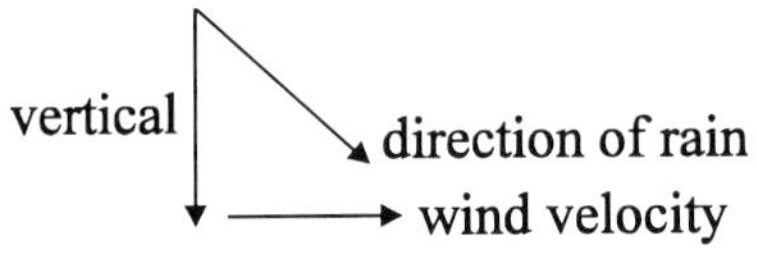

Velocities combine, like forces, according to the parallelogram rule.

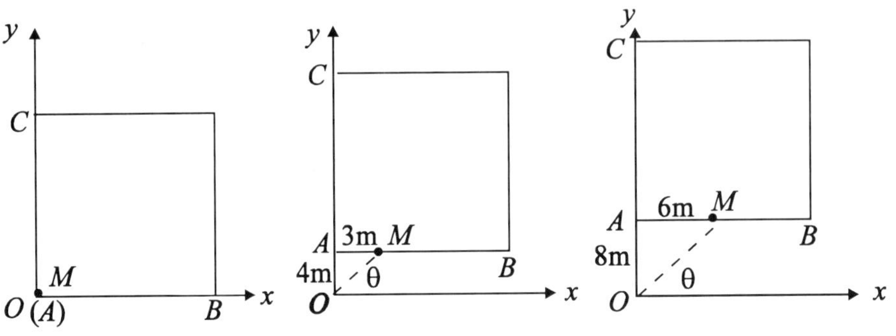

You can see this by imagining a large board on an ice rink and with two perpendicular edges *AB* and *AC* pointing East and North. Initially the board is placed, as shown in the diagram, with *A* at a fixed point *O* and *AB* and *AC* parallel to fixed lines drawn East and North through *O*. These lines are taken to be co-ordinate axes *Ox* and *Oy*. The board is then pulled northwards with speed 4 ms^{-1} and at the same time a small animal *M* is imagined to move along the line *AB* with speed 3 ms^{-1}. After 1 s, *OA* will be 4 m and *AM* will be 3 m so that, referred to the axes *Ox*, *Oy*, *M* will have coordinates (3,4) and *OM* will be $\sqrt{4^2+3^2}$ m = 5 m. After 2 s the coordinates will be (6, 8) and *OM* = 10 m. Therefore *M* will move along the line through *O* and the point (3, 4), its speed will be 5 ms^{-1}. Therefore the motion of *M* with speed 5 ms^{-1} at an angle θ to *Ox*, where $\tan\theta = \frac{4}{3}$ is a combination of the two separate motions i.e. the components of the velocity are 3 ms^{-1} along *Ox* and 4 ms^{-1} along *Oy*. This confirms the validity of the parallelogram of velocities in a simple case.
It is easier in more general motions to define the components in two perpendicular directions first rather than try and define directly something which represents the rate of change of position. If the components of velocity along *Ox* and *Oy* are defined by *u* and *v*,

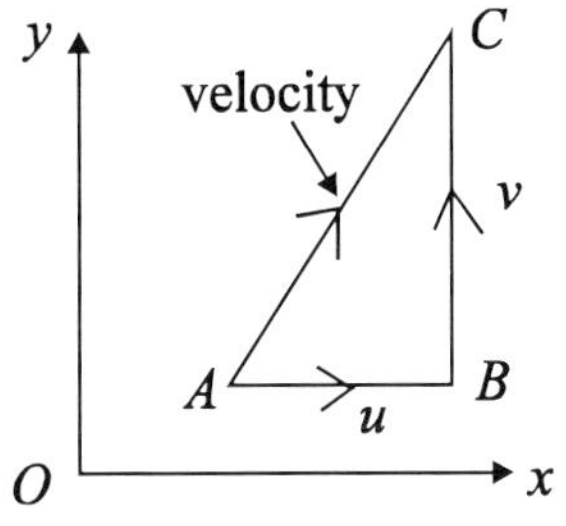

respectively, then the velocity is represented, as shown in the diagram, by the hypotenuse of the right angled triangle *ABC* where *AB* is parallel to *Ox* and proportional to *u* and *BC* is parallel to *Oy* and proportional to *v*. The length of the line *AC* represents the speed *w* which is defined by $w = \sqrt{u^2+v^2}$. The velocity is therefore defined to be of magnitude *w* and in the direction making an angle θ, where $\tan\theta = \frac{v}{u}$, with the positive *x* direction.

From the right angled triangle *ABC*, $\frac{u}{w} = \cos\theta$, $\frac{v}{w} = \sin\theta$,

i.e. $$u = w\cos\theta,\ v = w\sin\theta.$$

The above equations let you convert the magnitude-direction definition of velocity to component form and vice-versa.

The equations are precisely the same as those relating the magnitude and direction of a force to its components and you have to be careful, as in Statics in 2.3 in M1, that you choose the correct quadrant for the direction of the velocity.
The position of a particle moving in a plane is specified completely by its x and y co-ordinates; these may depend on time. These co-ordinates are generally referred to as the displacements of the particle from the origin. The x- and y-components of velocity, u and v respectively, are defined by

$$u = \frac{\mathrm{d}x}{\mathrm{d}t}, \qquad v = \frac{\mathrm{d}y}{\mathrm{d}t}.$$

If you have not yet covered differentiation, then the velocity components can be defined, as in 4.1 in M1, as the slopes of the graphs of x and y against time.
Therefore, given x and y, u and v can be found and therefore the magnitude (i.e. the speed) and direction of the velocity. As t varies, the point with co-ordinates x and y will describe a curve, the path of the particle, as shown in the diagram.

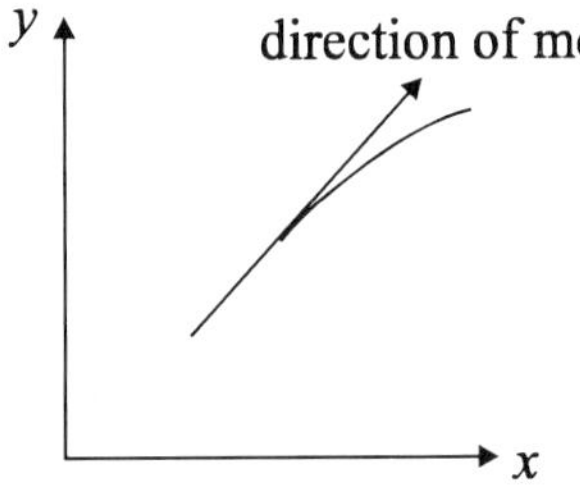

The motion of the particle will be at an angle θ to the x-axis where

$$\tan\theta = \frac{v}{u} = \frac{\frac{\mathrm{d}y}{\mathrm{d}t}}{\frac{\mathrm{d}x}{\mathrm{d}t}} = \frac{\mathrm{d}y}{\mathrm{d}x},$$

therefore the direction of motion of the particle will be along the tangent to the path.

Acceleration is also defined as a vector and its components are $\frac{\mathrm{d}^2x}{\mathrm{d}t^2}$ and $\frac{\mathrm{d}^2y}{\mathrm{d}t^2}$.
However the acceleration due to gravity is constant and vertically downwards and therefore, if the x and y axes are chosen horizontally and vertically, only one component of acceleration has to be considered in problems of motion under gravity as considered in 4.2.

Example 4.1

Find the x- and y-components of the following velocities
(i) 4 ms^{-1} at an angle of 40° to the positive x-axis,
(ii) 8 ms^{-1} at an angle of 140° to the positive x-axis,
(iii) 14 ms^{-1} at an angle of 60° below the positive x-axis.

The velocities are all shown in the diagram below where the x-axis is taken to be across the page to the right and the y-axis to be up the page.

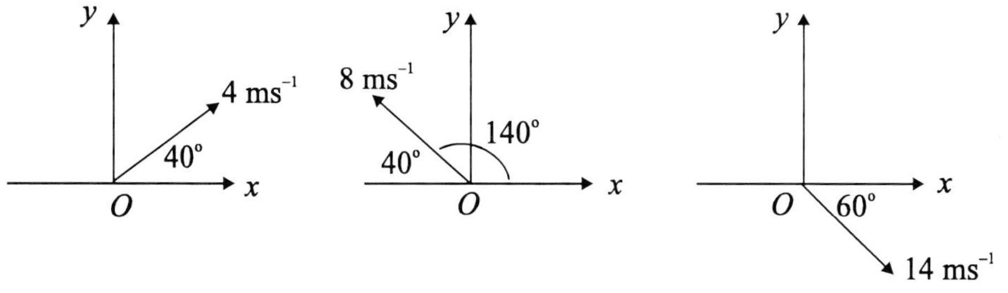

(i) (ii) (iii)

(i) The x- and y-components are

$$4\cos 40^\circ \text{ ms}^{-1} = 3.06 \text{ ms}^{-1} \text{ and } 4\sin 40^\circ \text{ ms}^{-1} = 2.57 \text{ ms}^{-1}.$$

(ii) The x- and y-components are

$$8\cos 140^\circ \text{ ms}^{-1} = -6.13\text{ms}^{-1} \text{ and } 8\sin 140^\circ \text{ ms}^{-1} = 5.14 \text{ ms}^{-1}.$$

These components could also have been found, as in problems in Statics, by taking components along the positive y direction and the negative x direction.

These are $\quad 8\cos 40^\circ \text{ ms}^{-1} = 6.13 \text{ ms}^{-1}$ and $8\sin 40^\circ \text{ ms}^{-1} = 5.14 \text{ ms}^{-1}$.

The x-component is then found by changing the sign of the first component.

(iii) In this case the simplest way is to find the components along the positive x- and negative y-axes; these are

$$14\cos 60^\circ \text{ ms}^{-1} = 7 \text{ ms}^{-1} \text{ and } 14\sin 60^\circ\text{ms}^{-1}\, 1 = 12.1 \text{ ms}^{-1}$$

The x- and y-components are therefore 7 ms^{-1} and -12.1 ms^{-1}.

Example 4.2

Find the magnitude and direction of the following velocities given that their x- and y-components are respectively

(i) $6 \text{ ms}^{-1}, 3 \text{ ms}^{-1}$, (ii) $-7 \text{ ms}^{-1}, 5 \text{ ms}^{-1}$, (iii) $-2 \text{ ms}^{-1}, -3 \text{ ms}^{-1}$.

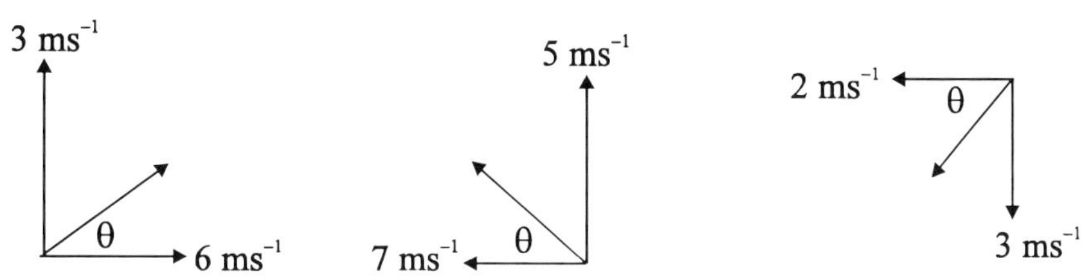

(i) (ii) (iii)

The components are shown in the above diagram where the x-axis is taken to be across the page to the right and the y-axis to be up the page.

(i) The speed is $\sqrt{6^2+3^2}$ ms^{-1} = 6.71 ms^{-1} and the motion is at an angle θ to the positive x-axis where $\tan\theta = \frac{3}{6}$ so that $\theta = 26.6^\circ$ and therefore the velocity is 6.71 ms^{-1} at an angle of 26.6° to the positive x-axis.

(ii) The speed is $\sqrt{7^2+5^2}$ ms^{-1} = 8.6 ms^{-1} and the motion is at an angle θ to the negative x-axis where $\tan\theta = \frac{5}{7}$ so that $\theta = 35.5°$ and therefore the velocity is 8.6 ms^{-1} at an angle of 144.5° to the positive x-axis.

(iii) The speed is $\sqrt{2^2+3^2}$ ms^{-1} = 3.61 ms^{-1} and the motion is at an angle θ to the negative x-axis in the third quadrant where $\tan\theta = \frac{3}{2}$ so that $\theta = 56.3°$ and therefore the velocity is 3.61 ms^{-1} at an angle of 236.3° to the positive x-axis.

Example 4.3

The x and y displacements, in metres, of a particle from the origin at time t s are $(3t,\ 4t - 3t^{-1})$. Find the velocity components when $t = 1$ and $t = 3$. Determine also the direction of motion for $t = 1$.

The velocity components are found by differentiating the displacements and this gives $u = 3$ ms^{-1}, $v = (4 - 6t)$ ms^{-1}. The velocity components for $t = 1$ are therefore 3 ms^{-1} and – 2 ms^{-1}, and for $t = 3$ are 3 ms^{-1} and – 14 ms^{-1}.

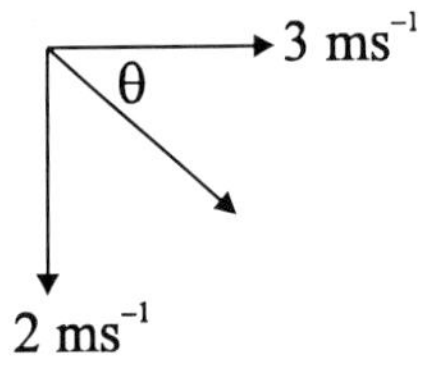

The components for $t = 1$ are shown in the diagram, with the x and y directions as defined in Example 4.2. The velocity is at an angle θ below the x-axis where $\tan\theta = \frac{2}{3}$ so that $\theta = 33.7^\circ$.

Exercises 4.1

In the following questions the x and y displacements of a particle from the origin are denoted by x m and y m respectively and the x- and y-components of velocity by u ms^{-1} and v ms^{-1} respectively.

1 Taking the x-axis to be across the page to the right and the y-axis to be up the page, find u and v in the following cases.

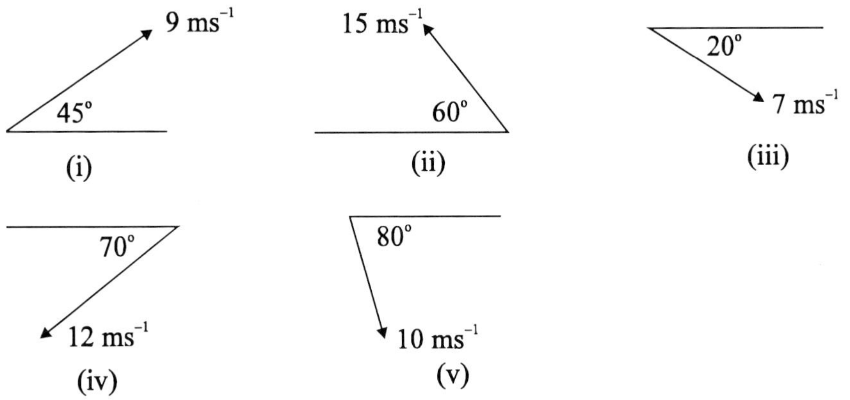

2 Find the magnitude and directions of the velocities corresponding to
(i) $u = 2, v = 6$, (ii) $u = -3, v = 8$, (iii) $u = 4, v = -12$, (iv) $u = -9, v = -4$,
(v) $u = 12, v = -15$.

3 Find u and v when
(i) $x = 5t,\ y = 2t + 4t^2$, (ii) $x = 3t,\ y = 4t - 3t^2$, (iii) $x = 8t^2,\ y = 5t^2 + 4t^3$,
(iv) $x = e^{-t},\ y = e^{-t} + e^{-2t}$.

4 Find the speed and the direction of motion for 3(i) and 3(ii) at $t = 2$.

4.2 Equations of motion

The motion of any body moving under gravity (such a motion is generally referred to as projectile motion with the moving body being called the projectile) is governed by Newton's second law of motion. You have already met this for motion along a line in the form mass × acceleration. The form for general motion is basically the same except that it is now necessary to take into account that the motion is no longer in a straight line. In more general circumstances Newton's law is

Mass × component of acceleration in any direction = component of force in that direction.

In projectile motion the **modelling assumptions** made are that all bodies are modelled as particles and that there are no resistive forces acting so that the only force acting is that due to gravity. If the x-axis is chosen horizontally and the y-axis vertically upwards then there is no x-component of force and the y-component of force is $-mg$, where g is the acceleration due to gravity. Therefore Newton's law gives

mass × x-component of acceleration = 0, mass × y-component of acceleration = $-mg$,

i.e. x-component of acceleration = 0, y-component of acceleration = $-g$.

The first equation shows that the x-component is a constant e.g. u, so that the horizontal displacement of a particle from its initial position is ut. The second equation shows that the vertical motion will be the same as that of a particle falling freely under gravity i.e. with downwards acceleration g. The vertical displacement can therefore be found from $s = ut + \frac{1}{2}at^2$ with $a = -g$ and u equal to the value of the upward velocity component at time $t = 0$; this will be denoted by v. Therefore the horizontal and vertical displacements at time t of a particle from a point O are given by

$$x = ut \quad \text{and} \quad y = vt - \frac{1}{2}gt^2,$$

where u and v are the components of the velocity of the particle at time $t = 0$ at the initial point O. Therefore if a particle were projected from O with velocity components u and v, as shown in the left hand diagram, its co-ordinates would be given by the above equations.

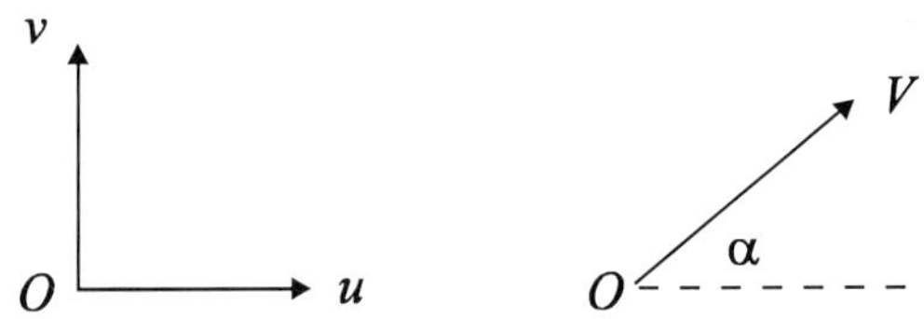

It is often more usual to give, as in the right hand diagram, the magnitude V and direction α to the horizontal of the initial velocity. Therefore $u = V\cos\alpha$, $v = V\sin\alpha$ and substituting into the expressions for the displacements gives

$$x = V\cos\alpha t \quad \text{and} \quad y = V\sin\alpha t - \frac{1}{2}gt^2.$$

Either of the above sets of equations can be used to solve any projectile problem but on the whole it is better to tackle any problem from first principles. It is important to notice that the equations determining the vertical and horizontal displacements are independent of each other. The horizontal motion is a motion at constant speed and the vertical motion is that of a particle moving vertically; you solved problems of this type in 4.3 in M1. The actual motion of the particle is the combination of the two independent motions.

It is also possible to generalise the principle of conservation of energy to cover projectile motion and use of this can give a quick method of finding speed. The principle of conservation of energy applies to the vertical motion in the form

$$\frac{1}{2}m\,(\text{vertical component of velocity})^2 + \text{gravitational P.E} = \text{constant.}$$

The horizontal component of velocity is constant and therefore the above equation holds if $\frac{1}{2}m$ (horizontal component of velocity)^2 is added to both sides. Also

$$(\text{horizontal component of velocity})^2 + (\text{vertical component of velocity})^2 = (\text{speed})^2.$$

The definition of kinetic energy can be generalised to plane motions by

$$\text{K.E.} = \frac{1}{2}m\,(\text{speed})^2,$$

and therefore with this definition the mechanical energy is conserved.

An alternative but completely equivalent way of finding the displacements would be to use the definition of acceleration in terms of a derivative to get

$$\frac{d^2x}{dt^2} = 0 \text{ and } \frac{d^2y}{dt^2} = -g.$$

These can be integrated to give x and y and obviously this again gives the same expressions as found directly from the constant acceleration formulae.

The expressions found for x and y above can be used to give some general formulae such as that for the greatest height risen. In many examinations full credit will not normally be given for using these formulae without derivation and this is stated in the M2 syllabus. These formulae are however useful in showing the general behaviour of a projectile and their derivation is given in 4.3.

Before working through some examples you may find it useful to have some general idea of the path of a projectile under the assumptions of the model. The actual path will be slightly different mainly due to the effect of air resistance. You will already have some idea of how a projectile moves from watching the motion of a football, tennis ball or cricket ball. You can get a particularly clear picture by looking at the water coming out of a hose pipe pointed at an angle.

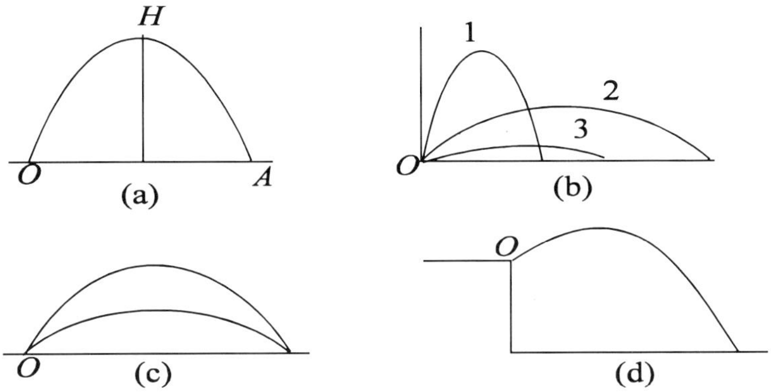

Diagram (a) shows the path taken by a projectile projected from level ground and landing on level ground. It rises to its highest point H and then hits the ground again, the curve described is known as a parabola and it is symmetric about the vertical line through its highest point H. At H the particle will be moving horizontally and, in view of the symmetry, the time to reach H will be one half of the time taken to reach A. The distance OA from ground to ground is called the range, R. Diagram (b) shows the variation in range with different angles of projection for a given speed of projection. Curve 1 shows that for a large angle of projection the range is relatively small. It increases as the angle of projection decreases until it reaches a maximum value for a projection angle of 45°, this is curve 2. Thereafter the range decreases with the angle of projection as shown by curve 3. Any range other than the maximum value can be attained for a given speed with two angles of projection; if α° is one such angle then $90^\circ - \alpha^\circ$ is the other. This is shown in diagram (c). If the particle is projected from the top of a cliff the path will be as in diagram (d).

The basic method of solving any problem is to write down the displacements from the point of projection at any time. These will involve the initial components of the velocity of projection, or equivalently, the speed and angle of projection. These will either be known or sufficient information will be given to find them. In cases of projection from ground level it is usually better to take the y-direction vertically upwards. For problems involving projection from a point above ground level it may be worth taking the y-direction downwards. In such a case you should remember to use the correct signs in $s = ut + \frac{1}{2}at^2$.

In all the following examples the horizontal and upwards vertical displacements of a particle at time t s are denoted by x m and y m respectively and u ms^{-1} and v ms^{-1} denote the horizontal and vertical components of the initial velocity and g will be assumed to be 9.8 ms^{-2}.

Example 4.4

A particle is projected from a point O on level ground with velocity components of 7 ms^{-1} horizontally and 19.6 ms^{-1} vertically upwards. Find the distance from O of the point where the particle next hits the ground and also find the greatest height reached above O.

Since there is no horizontal component of acceleration, the horizontal component of velocity has the constant value 7 and therefore

$$x = 7t.$$

Applying $s = ut + \frac{1}{2}at^2$ with $a = -9.8$, $u = 19.6$ gives

$$y = 19.6t - 4.9^2.$$

The particle is on the ground when $y = 0$ i.e.

$$19.6t - 4.9t^2 = 0,$$

so that $t = 0$ or $t = 4$, so it next hits the ground when $t = 4$ and $x = 28$. The greatest height is reached at the point where there is no vertical velocity. Applying $v = u + at$ with $u = 19.6$ and $a = -9.8$ shows that the vertical velocity v is given by

$$v = 19.6 - 9.8t.$$

This vanishes when $t = 2$. This result could also have been deduced from the symmetry about the vertical through the point of greatest height. Substituting $t = 2$ into the expression for y gives the greatest height as (39.2 – 19.6) m = 19.6 m.

An alternative method for finding the greatest height would have been to use $v^2 = u^2 + 2as$, with $u = 19.6$, $a = -9.8$ and $v = 0$.

Example 4.5

A particle is projected from a point O with a speed of 25 ms^{-1} at an angle θ to the horizontal where $\tan\theta = \frac{4}{3}$. Find the equation of the path of the particle and also its direction of motion when $t = 3$.

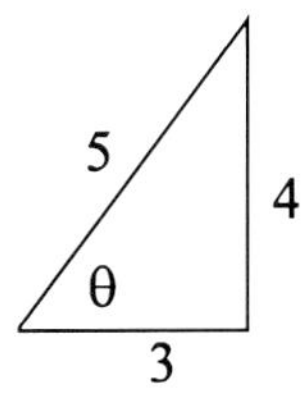

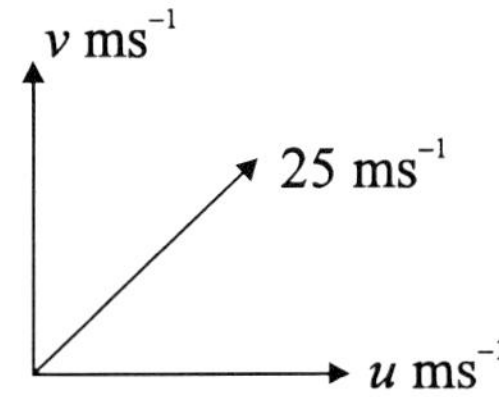

The left hand diagram shows that $\cos\theta = \frac{3}{5}$ and $\sin\theta = \frac{4}{5}$, it then follows from the right hand diagram that the horizontal component of velocity is $25\cos\theta = 15$ and the vertical component of velocity is $25\sin\theta = 20$.

The horizontal component of velocity will have the constant value 15 and therefore

$$x = 15\,t.$$

Applying $s = ut + \frac{1}{2}at^2$ with $a = -9.8$, $u = 20$ gives

$$y = 20t - 4.9t^2.$$

Substituting for t in terms of x gives

$$y = \frac{20}{15}x - 4.9\frac{x^2}{225} = \frac{4}{3}x - \frac{4.9x^2}{225},$$

which is the equation of the path.

The vertical component of velocity is found by substituting $u = 20$ and $a = -9.8$ into $v = u + at$ giving

$$20 - 9.8t.$$

(This could also have been obtained by differentiating y with respect to t.)

For $t = 3$ the vertical component of velocity is -9.4 and the components of the velocity are as shown in the diagram.

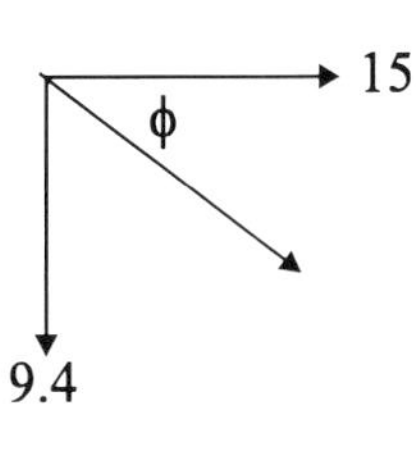

The particle is therefore moving at an angle ϕ below the horizontal where $\tan\phi = 0.63$, so that $\phi = 32.1°$.

The direction could also have been obtained by differentiating the equation of the path with respect to x and finding the gradient for $t = 3$ i.e. for $x = 45$.

$$\frac{dy}{dx} = \frac{4}{3} - \frac{9.8x}{225},$$

and its value for $x = 45$ is -0.63. The minus sign shows that it is moving below the horizontal.

Example 4.6

A ball is projected from ground level so that after 2 s it just clears a wall at a distance of 6 m away and 3 m high. Find the initial horizontal and vertical components of velocity.

In this case the initial components of velocity are not given but, as in the previous examples, the co-ordinates can be expressed in terms of them as

$$x = ut.$$

$$y = vt - 4.9t^2.$$

The conditions give $x = 6$ for $t = 2$, and substituting into the equation for x gives $u = 3$.

Substituting $t = 2$ and $y = 3$ into the equation for y gives

$$3 = 2v - 4.9 \times 4,$$

so that $v = 11.3$.

Example 4.7

A golf ball is projected from the ground with speed 35 ms^{-1} at an angle θ to the horizontal where $\tan\theta = \frac{3}{4}$. On its downward path it just clears a tree 5.6 m high. Find the distance of the tree from the point of projection.

The horizontal and vertical components of velocity are given by $u = 35\cos\theta$ and $v = 35\sin\theta$. Since $\tan\theta = \frac{3}{4}$, it follows by drawing a right angled triangle as in example 4.5 that $\cos\theta = \frac{4}{5}$ and $\sin\theta = \frac{3}{5}$ so that $u = 28$ and $v = 21$.

The displacements from the initial point are given by

$$x = 28t.$$

$$y = 21t - 4.9t^2.$$

Substituting $y = 5.6$ into the expression for y gives

$$5.6 = 21t - 4.9t^2.$$

This is a quadratic equation for t, this can be solved using the standard formula and the roots are $t = 4$ and $t = 0.29$. The question states that the ball hits the tree on its downwards path so the correct root is the larger one i.e. $t = 4$. Substituting this into the expression for x gives the distance to the foot of the tree as 112 m.

Example 4.8

A particle is projected horizontally with speed 32 ms^{-1}, as shown in the diagram, from the top of a vertical cliff to horizontal ground at a distance of 80 m below the point of projection. Find the distance of the point of impact from the base of the cliff.

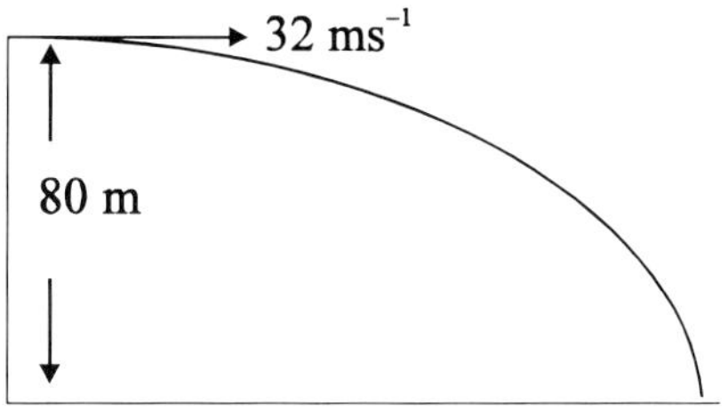

In this case, since the motion is entirely downwards, the y direction can be chosen vertically downwards. The initial vertical velocity is zero and therefore the displacements are given by

$$x = 32t,$$
$$y = 4.9t^2.$$

The particle hits the ground when $y = 80$ so that $80 = 4.9t^2$ giving $t = 4.04$. Substituting this in the expression for x shows that the particle hits the ground at a distance of 129.3 m from the base of the cliff.

Example 4.9

A particle is projected with speed 25 ms^{-1} and with an initial upwards component of velocity of magnitude 19.6 ms^{-1}, as shown in the diagram, from the top of a vertical cliff to horizontal ground at a distance of 58.8 m below the point of projection. Find
(i) the distance of the point of impact from the base of the cliff,
(ii) the speed of the particle on impact.

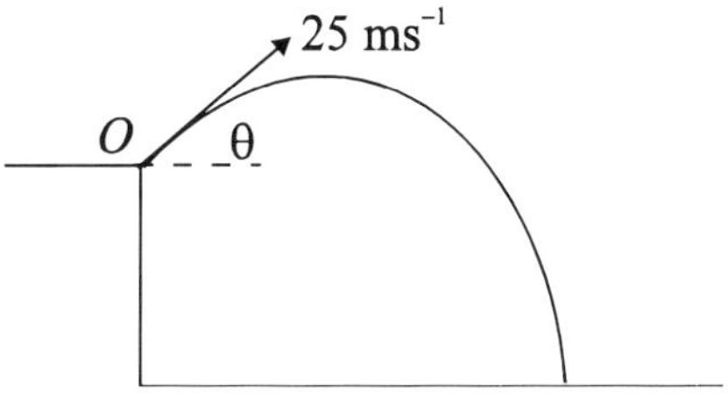

In this question v is given but not u. The angle of projection θ above the horizontal can be found from $19.6 = 25 \sin\theta$ which gives $\theta = 51.6^\circ$ and $u = 25\cos\theta = 15.52$. In this case the y direction will be taken upwards so that the displacements are

$$x = 15.52t.$$
$$y = 19.6\,t - 4.9t^2.$$

The particle hits the ground when $y = -58.8$ so that

$$-58.8 = 19.6t - 4.9t^2,$$

this equation simplifies to

$$t^2 - 4t - 12 = 0,$$

which factorises as

$$(t-6)(t+2) = 0.$$

The positive root is $t = 6$ and substituting this into the expression for x shows that the particle hits the ground at a distance of 91.2 m from the base of the cliff.

The speed V ms^{-1} on impact can be found using the principle of conservation of energy which gives

$$\frac{1}{2}m(25)^2 + m \times 9.8 \times 58.8 = \frac{1}{2}mV^2,$$

where m is the mass of the particle and the level of the base of the cliff has been taken as the zero level of potential energy. This equation gives $V = 42.16$.

Exercises 4.2

Questions 1 to 6 refer to a particle projected from the origin with horizontal and vertical components of velocity u ms^{-1} and v ms^{-1} (or with speed V ms^{-1} at an angle α above the horizontal), the displacements of the particle at time t s after projection are denoted by x m and y m, respectively. Also g should be taken as 9.8 ms^{-2}.

1 $u = 4$, $v = 5$, find x and y in terms of t and find when the particle is next at the level of projection and its horizontal displacement from the point of projection at this time.

2 $u = 6$, $v = 11$, find x and y in terms of t and find its maximum height above the level of projection.

3 $u = 4$, $v = 12$, find x and y in terms of t and find the magnitude and direction of its velocity when $t = 1$ and when $t = 8$.

4 $V = 25$, $\alpha = 30^\circ$, find x and y in terms of t and find when the particle is next at the level of projection and its horizontal displacement from the point of projection at this time.

5 $V = 30$, $\sin\alpha = \frac{3}{5}$, find x and y in terms of t and find its maximum height above the level of projection.

6 $V = 40$, $\alpha = 20^\circ$, find x and y in terms of t and find the magnitude and direction of its velocity when $t = 1$ and when $t = 8$.

7 One second after projection a particle has a horizontal component of velocity of 8 ms^{-1} and an upwards vertical velocity component of 25 ms^{-1}. Find the maximum height reached above the point of projection.

8 A ball is thrown with speed 20 ms^{-1} at an angle of 20° above the horizontal and just clears the top of a wall at a distance of 18 m from O. Find the height of the wall above the level of O.

9 A stone is thrown from the top of a cliff at a height 75 m above sea level with initial speed 25 ms^{-1} at an angle α above the horizontal, where $\cos\alpha = \frac{3}{5}$. Find the distance from the base of the cliff to the point where the stone hits the sea.

10 A particle projected from the origin and moving under gravity has coordinates (10, 5) two seconds later. Find its initial velocity components.

11 A particle projected from level ground rises to a height of 19.6 m above it. Find the vertical component of its initial velocity.

12 A stunt motor cyclist attempts to cross a river 60 m wide by taking off at a speed of 35 ms^{-1} from a ramp at an angle of 25° to the horizontal. Determine whether he will be able to cross. He estimates that air resistance will be such that the distance travelled will only be 60% of that predicted by the model neglecting air resistance. Find the minimum speed with which he should leave the ramp.

4.3 Basic projectile formulae

In this section some of the basic formulae for projectile motion will be derived and used to establish some of the properties of the path that were described in 4.2. You should be aware of these formulae and know how to derive them but in examinations it is likely that quoting them without proof could bring a penalty.

If a particle is projected from a point O with velocity of magnitude V acting at an angle α above the horizontal, then the horizontal and vertical components of its initial velocity are $V\cos\alpha$ and $V\sin\alpha$. The horizontal velocity remains constant and therefore the horizontal displacement is $V\cos\alpha t$.

For the vertical motion, applying $s = ut + \frac{1}{2}at^2$ with $a = -g$ and $u = V\sin\alpha$ shows that the vertical displacement is $y = V\sin\alpha t - \frac{1}{2}gt^2$.

Therefore the horizontal and vertical displacements x and y are given by

$$x = V\cos\alpha t, \quad y = V\sin\alpha t - \frac{1}{2}gt^2.$$

The particle will be on the same level as the point of projection at the time $t = T$ when $y = 0$ i.e.

$$V\sin\alpha T - \frac{1}{2}gT^2 = 0.$$

This gives, since the solution $T = 0$ refers to the initial position,

$$T = \frac{2V\sin\alpha}{g},$$

and T is often referred to as the time of flight. Substituting T into the expression for x gives, for a particle projected from ground level, the distance of the point of impact from the point of projection. This is referred to as the range R which is therefore defined by

$$R = \frac{2V^2 \sin\alpha\cos\alpha}{g}.$$

You know from the symmetry properties of the trigonometric functions that

$$\sin\left(\frac{\pi}{2} - \alpha\right) = \cos\alpha \text{ and } \cos\left(\frac{\pi}{2} - \alpha\right) = \sin\alpha,$$

therefore if a particular value of α gives a range R then so will $\frac{\pi}{2} - \alpha$. It will be shown in P3 that $2 \sin\alpha \cos\alpha = \sin 2\alpha$ and therefore the maximum value of R, for a given V, occurs when $\sin 2\alpha = 1$, i.e. when $\alpha = \frac{\pi}{4}$. A proof, not depending on anything in P3, that the maximum value of range occurs for $\alpha = \frac{\pi}{4}$ is given at the end of this section.

Substituting $u = V \sin\alpha$ and $a = -g$ into $v = u + at$ gives the vertical component of the velocity to be $V \sin\alpha - gt$, this vanishes at the point of maximum height above O. Therefore the time to reach this point is $\frac{V\sin\alpha}{g}$, which is half the time of flight. Substituting this value into the expression for y shows that the greatest height h is given by

$$h = \frac{V^2\sin^2\alpha}{2g}.$$

(This could also have been obtained by substituting $v = 0$, $u = V \sin\alpha$ and $a = -g$ into $v^2 = u^2 + 2as$.)

Substituting the value of the time to the point of greatest height into the expression for x shows that the displacement of the point of greatest height is $\frac{1}{2}R$.

Eliminating t between the expressions for x and y gives

$$y = x\tan\alpha - \frac{gx^2}{2V^2\cos^2\alpha} = x\tan\alpha - \frac{gx^2}{2V^2}\sec^2\alpha,$$

which is the equation of the path of the particle.

You can check, by expanding the squared term in brackets, that the equation of the path can be rewritten as

$$y = -\frac{g\sec^2\alpha}{2V^2}\left(x - \frac{V^2\sin\alpha\cos\alpha}{g}\right)^2 + \frac{V^2\sin^2\alpha}{2g}$$

This can be further simplified to

$$y - h = -\frac{g\sec^2\alpha}{2V^2}\left(x - \frac{1}{2}R\right)^2,$$

this shows the symmetry about the point $x = \frac{1}{2}R$ i.e. the curve is symmetric about the vertical through the point of greatest height.

Determination of angle for maximum range

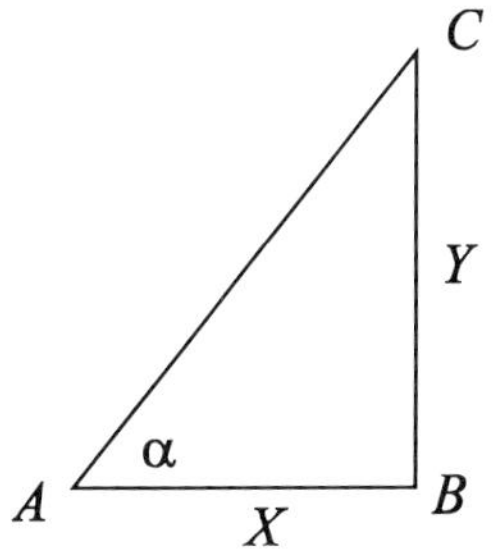

The diagram shows a right angled triangle ABC with the angle $BAC = \alpha$ and $AB = X$ and $BC = Y$. Therefore $\sin\alpha = \dfrac{Y}{\sqrt{X^2 + Y^2}}$, $\cos\alpha = \dfrac{X}{\sqrt{X^2 + Y^2}}$ and

$$2\sin\alpha\cos\alpha = \frac{2XY}{(X^2 + Y^2)}.$$

Also $$(X - Y)^2 = X^2 + Y^2 - 2XY.$$

The left hand side is positive and attains its minimum value of zero when $X = Y$, therefore

$$\frac{2XY}{(X^2 + Y^2)} \leq 1,$$

with the equality holding for $X = Y$. This therefore shows that $2\sin\alpha\cos\alpha$ has its maximum value when $\cos\alpha = \sin\alpha = \frac{1}{\sqrt{2}}$, i.e. for $\alpha = \frac{\pi}{4}$.

You may now care to use these results to answer Examples 4.4 and 4.5 and question 1, 2, 5 and 6 of Exercises 4.2.

Miscellaneous Exercises 4

1 A golf ball is struck from a point O on horizontal ground so that initially it is moving with speed 25 ms^{-1} at an angle θ to the horizontal where $\tan\theta = \frac{3}{4}$.

Write down expressions for the horizontal and vertical components of its displacement from O at any subsequent time t.

State two physical assumptions that you have made in determining the displacements. Determine the time to reach maximum height and the range as predicted by your model.

2(a) A zoo-keeper fires a tranquillising dart at a rhinoceros. The dart is fired at a speed of 25 ms^{-1} at an angle α above the horizontal and, when it hits the rhinoceros, it is at the same height as that at which it was fired.

Given that $\cos\alpha = \frac{7}{25}$ and $\sin\alpha = \frac{24}{25}$ find

(i) the time of flight of the dart,

(ii) how close the keeper was to the rhinoceros when the dart was fired.

(The dart is to be modelled as a particle and air resistance may be neglected.)

(b) The zoo-keeper has to tranquillize another rhinoceros well beyond the range of the dart but which is running towards the keeper at a speed of 10 ms^{-1}. The keeper fires the dart at the same speed and angle of projection as in (a). How far away should the rhinoceros be from the zoo-keeper when the dart is fired?

3(a) At time $t = 0$ a particle P is projected from a point O on horizontal ground with speed 40 ms^{-1} at an angle α to the horizontal, where $\cos\alpha = \frac{3}{5}$.

Write down expressions for its vertical and horizontal displacements from O at time t seconds and show that it reaches its greatest height after approximately 3.27 s.

Some time after attaining its greatest height the particle hits a screen, which is perpendicular to its plane of motion, at a point B at a height 49.6 m above the horizontal.

(i) Show that the particle hits the screen 4 seconds after being projected.

(ii) Find the gradient of the path immediately before impact.

(b) The screen is then moved nearer to O so that the particle, when projected as above, still strikes it at the point B. Find, in metres correct to one decimal place, the perpendicular distance of the screen from O in this case.

(c) The screen is moved to the position where P, when projected as above, strikes it at the highest point of its motion. Given that the coefficient of restitution between the particle and the screen is $\frac{1}{4}$ find, in metres correct to one decimal place, the perpendicular distance from the screen to the point where P first hits the ground.

4 A particle P is projected from a point O on a horizontal plane with speed v at an angle α above the horizontal. It rises to a maximum height h above the plane and strikes the plane again at a distance r from O. Write down x and y, the horizontal and vertical displacements of P from O at time t after projection, in terms of v, α, g and t. Hence find r and h in terms of v, g and α.

The particle passes through the point A whose horizontal displacement from O is pr, $(0 < p < 0.5)$. Find, in terms of p and α, the tangent of the angle β between the horizontal and the path of the particle at A. State the horizontal displacement of the point B where the path is inclined at an angle β below the horizontal.

Given that at A the particle is at a height a above the horizontal plane, express a in terms of p and h.

5 A golf ball is driven from a point O with an initial speed of 42 ms^{-1} at an angle α to the horizontal. Neglecting air resistance, derive the horizontal component x and the vertical component y, of the ball's displacement from O at time t after projection. Show that

$$y = x \tan \alpha - \frac{x^2}{360\cos^2 a}.$$

The golf ball just clears a tree at B where B is on the same horizontal level as O and OB is 150 m. The tree is 5 m high. Verify that one value of α is such that $\tan \alpha = \frac{3}{5}$.

By using the identity $\frac{1}{\cos^2 a} = 1 + \tan^2 \alpha$, find a quadratic equation satisfied by $\tan \alpha$ and hence find a second value of $\tan \alpha$ such that the ball just clears the tree at B.

6 A particle, projected with speed V at an angle α to the horizontal from O, moves freely under gravity. Find u and v, the horizontal and vertical components of its velocity, and x and y, its horizontal and vertical displacements, respectively, at time t after projection. Show that

$$2\frac{y}{x} - \frac{v}{u} = \tan \alpha.$$

Given that the particle strikes a plane through the point of projection and inclined at an angle β to the horizontal, where $\tan \beta = \frac{1}{2}$ at right angles, find the value of the ratio $\frac{v}{u}$ at the instant of impact. Hence find the value of $\tan \alpha$.

7 A particle P is projected with speed V at an angle α to the horizontal from O. Find u and v, the horizontal and vertical components of its velocity, and x and y, its horizontal and vertical displacements, respectively, at time t after projection. Given that the particle strikes the horizontal plane through O after a time T, show that

$$T = \frac{2V \sin\alpha}{g}.$$

Find, in terms of g and T, the maximum height of the particle above the level of O.

Given that at time $\frac{5T}{8}$ the particle is moving at right angles to its original direction of motion, find $\tan \alpha$.

8 A particle is projected from a point O on level ground and next strikes the ground again after a time T at the point A, where $OA = 2a$. Find the horizontal and vertical components of the velocity of projection.

9 A stone is projected with a velocity of 14.7 ms^{-1} at an angle α to the horizontal, where $\sin\alpha = \frac{3}{5}$. Before reaching its maximum height it just misses the top of a pole of height 2 m. At the instant the stone is thrown a bird leaves the top of the pole and flies horizontally at a constant speed of v ms^{-1}. Find v given that the stone hits the bird.

10 Two seconds after a stone is thrown, it is moving at an angle α to the horizontal where $\tan\alpha = 2$, a further second later it is moving at an angle β to the horizontal, where $\tan\beta = 1$.

Find, by considering the ratio $\frac{\tan\alpha}{\tan\beta}$, the vertical component of the initial velocity of projection. Determine also the horizontal component of the initial velocity of projection.

11 A particle is projected from a point with speed 25 ms^{-1} at an angle α to the horizontal where $\tan\alpha = \frac{7}{25}$. Find the magnitude and direction of the velocity of the particle two seconds after projection.

12 At a particular instant a particle P is projected from a point O with horizontal and upward components of velocity $3nu$ and $5nu$, respectively, where n and u are positive constants. At the same instant a second particle Q is projected from a point whose co-ordinates referred to O are $(16a, 17a)$, where the x-axis is horizontal and the y-axis is vertically upwards.

The initial x and y components of the velocity of Q are $-4u$ and $3u$, respectively.

Find the horizontal and vertical components of the displacements from O of P and Q at time t after projection and find the value of n such that the particles collide.

13(a) A particle is projected from a point O with speed u at an angle α above the horizontal.

(i) Write down expressions for the horizontal and vertical displacements of the particle from O at time t after projection,

(ii) deduce that the particle first hits the horizontal plane through O at a distance $\dfrac{2u^2 \sin\alpha\cos\alpha}{g}$ from O,

(iii) show that the greatest height reached by the particle above the level of O is $\dfrac{u^2 \sin^2\alpha}{2g}$.

(b) A particle P is projected from a point O with speed $\sqrt{12ga}$ at the angle which gives maximum range on the horizontal plane through O. Find the tangent of the angle between the velocity of P and the horizontal at time $\sqrt{\dfrac{3a}{8g}}$ after projection.

(c) A particle Q is projected with speed $\sqrt{12ga}$ from a point A on the horizontal floor of a room with a horizontal ceiling at a height $\dfrac{3a}{2}$ above the floor. Find, assuming that Q must not hit the ceiling, the maximum value of the distance from A of the point at which Q first hits the floor.

14

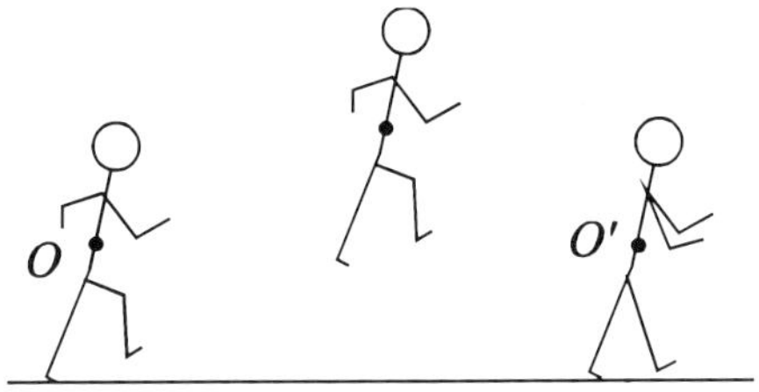

(a)

Diagram (a) shows a simplified schematic diagram of a model of the action of a long jumper. The points O and O' denote the positions of the centre of gravity of the jumper at the start and the end of the jump, respectively. In this model it is assumed that the points O and O' are on the same horizontal level and that the only force acting on the jumper during the jump is the force due to gravity. The jumper is taken to be a particle occupying the position of his centre of gravity and projected at time $t = 0$ s with speed V at an angle α to the horizontal. The horizontal and vertical components of the displacement from O at time t are denoted by x and y respectively. Write down expressions for x and y at time t and hence show that

$$y = px - qx^2,$$

where p and q are constants which should be found in terms of V, g and α.

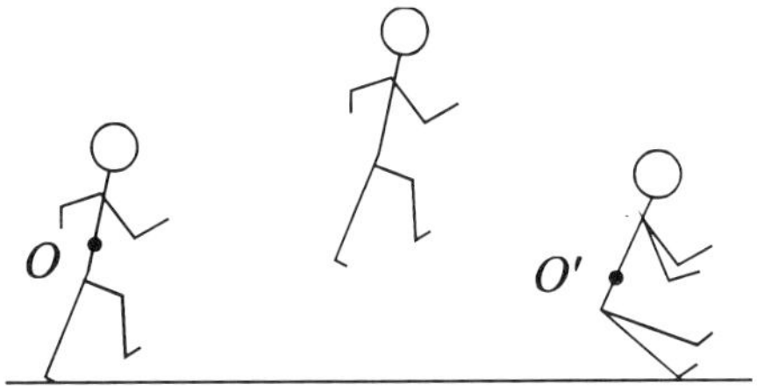

(b)

Diagram (b) shows a more realistic model where it is assumed that the centre of gravity of the jumper drops a vertical distance of 0.3 m between take-off and landing. In one particular instance the values of α and V (which you do not need to find) are such that the above equation, with x and y measured in metres, becomes

$$y = \frac{4}{3}x - \frac{2}{9}x^2.$$

Find the difference between the horizontal displacement of the centre of gravity between take-off and landing calculated using this second model and that calculated using the first model.

15 A golf ball is at rest at a point A on horizontal ground. Some distance away is a tree, 17.5 m high. The golf ball is struck so that the horizontal and vertical components of its initial velocity are 24.5 ms^{-1} and 28 ms^{-1} respectively. The golf ball just clears the top of the tree when it is on the downward part of its flight. Find

(a) the time taken by the ball to reach the top of the tree,

(b) the distance of the base of the tree from A,

(c) the distance of the base of the tree from the point where the ball strikes the ground.

16 A particle P is projected with speed 49 ms^{-1} at an angle α to the horizontal from O. Find x and y, its horizontal and vertical displacements, respectively, at time t s after projection. Hence show that for $x = 140$

$$y = 140 \tan \alpha - 40 \sec^2 \alpha.$$

The particle just clears a wall 20 m high at a distance of 140 m from the point of projection. Find, by using the result $\sec^2 \alpha = 1 + \tan^2 \alpha$, the two values of $\tan \alpha$ for which this is possible.

17 A point O is vertically above a fixed point A of a horizontal plane and a particle P is projected from O with speed $5V$ at an angle α above the horizontal, where $\cos \alpha = \frac{3}{5}$. It hits the plane at a point B at a distance $\frac{48V^2}{g}$ from A. Show that the height of O above A is $\frac{64V^2}{g}$ and find the distance of P from O when it is directly level with it.

A second particle is now projected with speed $24W$ from O at an angle α above the horizontal and it also hits the plane at B. Find an equation involving V, W, g and α. Given that one value of α is 45°, find V in terms of W and show that the other value of α is such that

$$7 \tan^2 \alpha - 6 \tan \alpha - 1 = 0.$$

18 A particle is projected from a point O on a horizontal plane with speed u in a direction making an angle α above the horizontal. At a subsequent time t, the horizontal and vertical displacements of the particle from O are denoted by x and y, respectively, and it is moving in a direction inclined at an angle β above the horizontal, with the upward vertical component of its velocity being v.

(a) Show, from the equations of motion, that

(i) $v + u \sin \alpha = \dfrac{2y}{t}$,

(ii) $x(\tan \alpha + \tan \beta) = 2y$.

(b) When moving at an angle of 45° above the horizontal, the particle just clears a wall of height 3 m and at a perpendicular distance of 2 m from O. The wall is perpendicular to the plane of motion of the particle. Subsequently, when moving at an angle of 45° below the horizontal, the particle just clears a second identical and parallel wall. Find

(i) $\tan \alpha$,

(ii) the distance between the walls,

(iii) the range on the horizontal plane through O,

(iv) the maximum height reached above the plane.

Chapter 5

Vectors

After working through this chapter you should

- know what is meant by a vector,
- be familiar with the representation of a vector in terms of its cartesian components,
- be able to use the cartesian representation to find the magnitude of a vector and to add and subtract vectors,
- be able to calculate the scalar product of two vectors,
- be able to differentiate and integrate a vector in cartesian component form with respect to a parameter.

The aim in this Chapter is to give the basic principles underlying the use of vectors so that these can be applied to various areas of Mechanics.

Essentially, this Chapter contains the Pure Mathematics necessary to use vectors in the remainder of the Mechanics course.

5. 1 Vectors and scalars

Scalars

A scalar is a quantity which is represented only by one number, generally its magnitude. Most of the quantities that you have met so far such as mass, speed and distance are scalars.

Vectors

A vector is a quantity which has both magnitude and direction. The simplest example of a vector is the distance and direction of a point B from another point A.

This is called the displacement of B from A and extends the idea of displacement as defined in Chapter 1 of M1 to more than one dimension. The displacement of one point from another is sometimes given in a direct form such as saying that a point B is 5 km North of another point A, as shown in the left-hand diagram below.

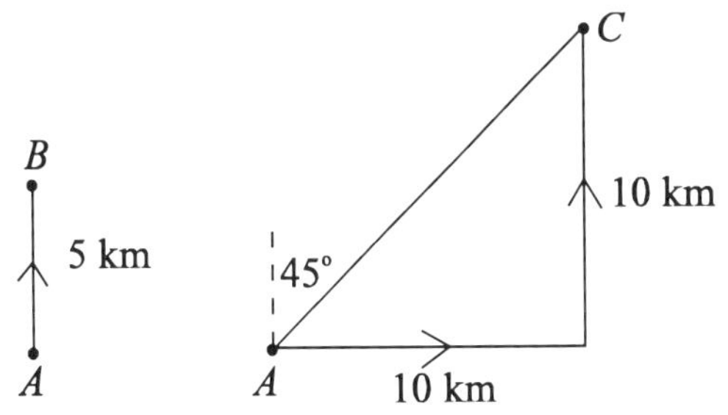

Alternatively, the displacement can be given less directly by, for example, saying a plane travels 10 km East from A, then turns and travels 10 km North to the point C as shown in the right-hand diagram on the previous page. In this case the displacement of C from A is $\sqrt{10^2+10^2} = 14.1$ km on a bearing of 45°.

A line joining two points with the sense being defined from one point to the other is called a directed line segment. Any vector can be fully represented by a directed line segment since this has magnitude, its length, and direction, the sense in which the line is travelling. The notation $\overrightarrow{AB}$ is used to describe the line segment joining A to B in the sense from A to B. Equivalently, the line segment joining A to B in the sense from A to B is said to define the vector $\overrightarrow{AB}$. Similarly $\overrightarrow{BA}$ is used to describe the line segment joining A to B in the sense from B to A.

A vector is not generally fixed in space and the three parallel and equal line segments $\overrightarrow{AB}$, $\overrightarrow{CD}$, $\overrightarrow{EF}$ in the diagram all represent the same vector.

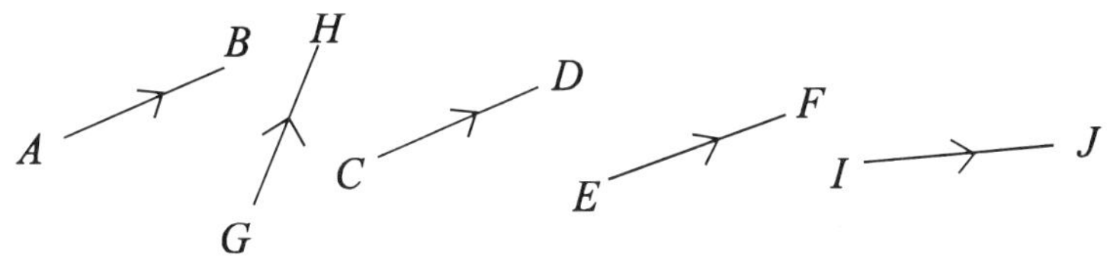

The other two line segments $\overrightarrow{GH}$ and $\overrightarrow{IJ}$, which are of the same length as the other line segments, do not represent the same vector as they have different directions.

You have already met in your course, forces, which are vectors, in that they have both magnitude and direction.

Vector notation

There are essentially two different notations for vectors and the notation that you will use in writing vectors is not usually the one that is convenient to use in books.

The displacement of B from A is often written, using the above notation for a line segment, as $\overrightarrow{AB}$. The length of the displacement, a scalar, is written as $|\overrightarrow{AB}|$ or sometimes just as AB. Quite often a single letter is used to denote a vector and it is shown in print in bold, i.e. dark type, as $\boldsymbol{a}$. The magnitude, or modulus, of a vector is a scalar and is written as $|\boldsymbol{a}|$ or a.

In writing it is difficult to show darker letters and so a vector is shown by underlining e.g. $\underline{a}$, or by using a wavy underline, e.g. $\underset{\sim}{a}$, or by writing an arrow above it, e.g. $\overrightarrow{\boldsymbol{a}}$.

The magnitude of a vector is shown by writing $|\underline{a}|$, $|\underset{\sim}{a}|$, $|\overrightarrow{\boldsymbol{a}}|$ or a. Whatever notation you use, it is extremely important in anything that you write that you should show clearly the difference between a vector and a scalar.

Position vector

In many problems most measurements are referred to some origin O. The displacement $\overrightarrow{OP}$, is referred to as the position vector of P relative to O and is often denoted by $\boldsymbol{r}$, and its magnitude is r. The vector $\overrightarrow{AB}$ can be interpreted as the positon vector of B relative to A.

5.2 Properties of vectors

Magnitude of a vector

The magnitude of a vector is the length of the line segment representing it.

Equal vectors

Two vectors are defined to be equal if they are of the same magnitude and act in the same direction. The vectors represented in the diagram above by the two parallel and equal line segments $\overrightarrow{AB}$ and $\overrightarrow{CD}$ are equal. Equivalently, the line segments are two representations of the same vector.

Negative vectors

The vector $-\boldsymbol{a}$ is in the opposite direction to the vector $\boldsymbol{a}$ but of the same magnitude.

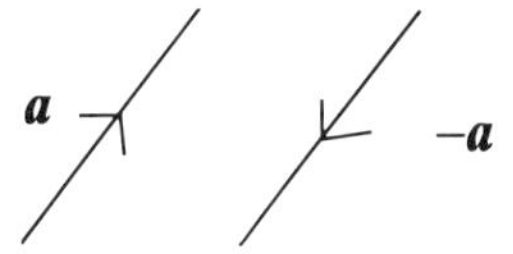

This is shown in the diagram and you have met this idea with forces. Similarly

$$\overrightarrow{BA} = -\overrightarrow{AB}.$$

Multiplication by a scalar and vectors in the same and opposite directions

The vector $m\,\boldsymbol{a}$, where m is a positive scalar, is a vector in the same direction as $\boldsymbol{a}$ but of magnitude $m\,a$ or $m\,|\,\boldsymbol{a}\,|$. The vector $m\,\boldsymbol{a}$, where m is a negative scalar, is a vector in the opposite direction to $\boldsymbol{a}$ but of magnitude $|\,m\,|\,a$ or $|\,m\,|\,|\,\boldsymbol{a}\,|$.

It is particularly important when you come to write expressions like $m\,\boldsymbol{a}$ to show clearly, by underlining, which is the vector. If you don't do this you will have expressions like ma and have a scalar when you should have a vector.

Vectors which are in the same, or opposite directions, are said to be parallel.

The vectors $\boldsymbol{a}$, $2\boldsymbol{a}$ and $-2\boldsymbol{a}$ are shown in the diagram.

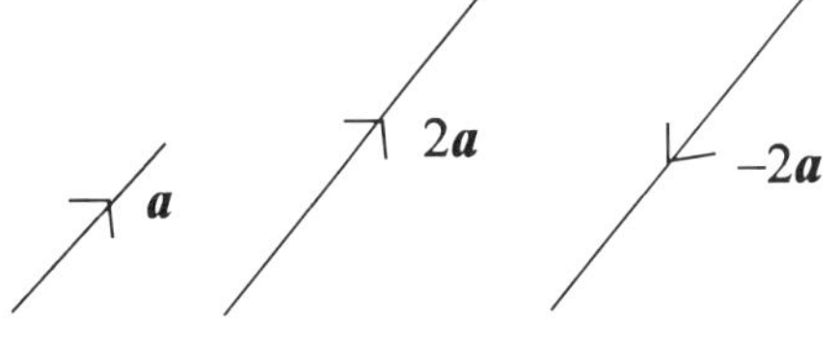

Unit vectors

A unit vector is one of unit magnitude. The unit vector in the direction of the vector $\boldsymbol{a}$ is found by dividing $\boldsymbol{a}$ by its magnitude and is therefore $\frac{\boldsymbol{a}}{a}$. Alternatively if $\boldsymbol{n}$ denotes the unit vector in the direction of a vector $\boldsymbol{a}$ then $\boldsymbol{a} = a\boldsymbol{n}$ or, equivalently, $|\,\boldsymbol{a}\,|\,\boldsymbol{n}$.

Addition and subtraction of vectors

The law of addition of vectors is the same as the combination of displacements. If you travel from A to B and then from B to C you will have been displaced from A to C.

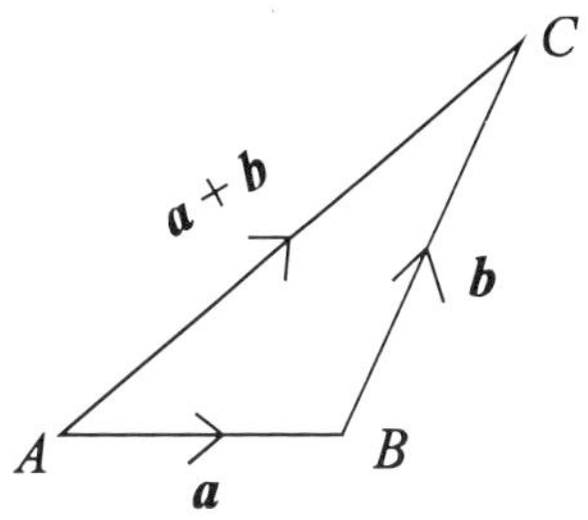

The sum of the displacements $\overrightarrow{AB}$ and $\overrightarrow{BC}$ is the displacement $\overrightarrow{AC}$. That is

$$\overrightarrow{AB} + \overrightarrow{BC} = \overrightarrow{AC}.$$

Therefore if $\overrightarrow{AB}$ represents the vector $\boldsymbol{a}$ and $\overrightarrow{BC}$ represents the vector $\boldsymbol{b}$ then $\overrightarrow{AC}$ represents the vector $\boldsymbol{a} + \boldsymbol{b}$. This is the triangle law which you have already met for forces. The sum $\boldsymbol{a} + \boldsymbol{b}$ is sometimes referred to, as for forces, as the **resultant** of $\boldsymbol{a}$ and $\boldsymbol{b}$.

This definition can be extended to show how several vectors can be added together, a pair of vectors is added together, then a further vector can be added etc. The left hand diagram shows the sum $\boldsymbol{a} + \boldsymbol{b} + \boldsymbol{c}$ of the three vectors $\boldsymbol{a}$, $\boldsymbol{b}$ and $\boldsymbol{c}$.

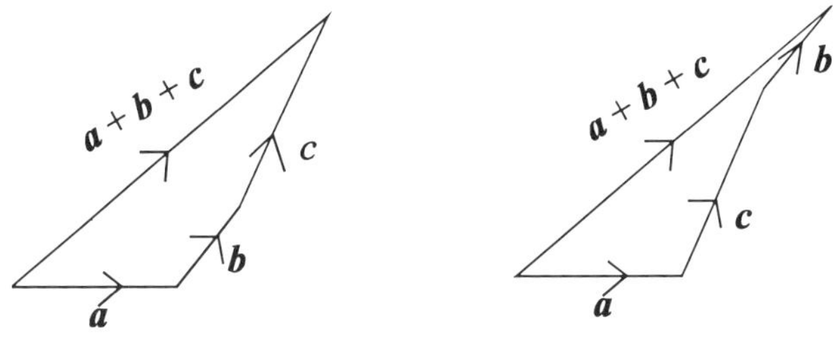

The order in which the vectors are added does not matter as can be seen from the right hand diagram.

It is important to realise that, before assuming that physical quantities like force can be added using the triangle law, it is necessary to verify experimentally that this is the case. Subtraction is defined by

$$\boldsymbol{b} - \boldsymbol{a} \;=\; \boldsymbol{b} + (-\,\boldsymbol{a}).$$

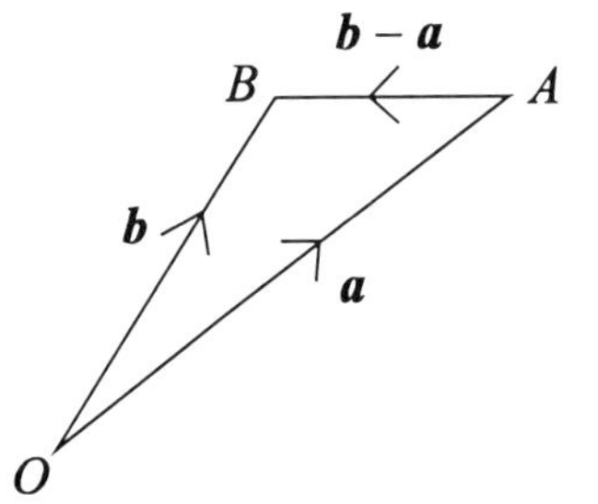

In the diagram the position vectors of A and B are $\boldsymbol{a}$ and $\boldsymbol{b}$, respectively, and therefore the vector $-\boldsymbol{a}$ can be represented by $\overrightarrow{AO}$. Therefore $\boldsymbol{b}-\boldsymbol{a}$ is represented by

$$\overrightarrow{AO} + \overrightarrow{OB} = \overrightarrow{AB}$$

i.e. $$\overrightarrow{AB} = \boldsymbol{b} - \boldsymbol{a}.$$

This could have been found also from the triangle law which shows that

$$\overrightarrow{OA} + \overrightarrow{AB} = \overrightarrow{OB}$$

i.e. $$\boldsymbol{a} + \overrightarrow{AB} = \boldsymbol{b},$$

and moving $\boldsymbol{a}$ to the right hand side gives $\overrightarrow{AB}$.

It is important to notice that vectors can be moved across equals signs, provided the sign is changed, just like scalars.

Also vectors obey the normal algebraic rules like scalars i.e.

$$p\boldsymbol{a} + q\boldsymbol{a} = (p+q)\boldsymbol{a}, \quad p\boldsymbol{a} + q\boldsymbol{a} + r\boldsymbol{b} + s\boldsymbol{b} = (p+q)\boldsymbol{a} + (r+s)\boldsymbol{b},$$

i.e. in adding vectors you can add the coefficients of the vectors exactly the same as in normal algebra.

Representing vectors

It is possible to write any two dimensional vector $\boldsymbol{c}$ as the sum of any two non parallel vectors. This can be seen from the following diagram where $\boldsymbol{c}$ is represented by $\overrightarrow{OC}$.

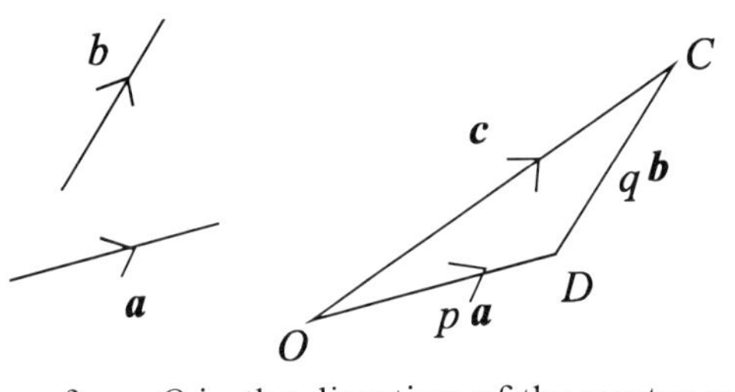

If a line is drawn from O in the direction of the vector $\boldsymbol{a}$ and one drawn from C in the direction of the vector $\boldsymbol{b}$ then the lines will intersect at D. Also, by the definition of scalar multiplication, $\overrightarrow{OD} = p\boldsymbol{a}$ and $\overrightarrow{DC} = q\boldsymbol{b}$, where p and q are scalars. The triangle law then shows that $\boldsymbol{c} = p\boldsymbol{a} + q\boldsymbol{b}$. The vectors $p\boldsymbol{a}$ and $q\boldsymbol{b}$ are called component vectors of $\boldsymbol{c}$. Their magnitudes, i.e. the lengths OD and DC, are called the components of $\boldsymbol{c}$ in the direction of the vectors $\boldsymbol{a}$ and $\boldsymbol{b}$ respectively.

This representation, when $\boldsymbol{a}$ and $\boldsymbol{b}$ are perpendicular to each other, is the basis for the use of cartesian components described in section 5.3.

Example 5.1

The diagram shows two points A and B with position vectors $\boldsymbol{a}$ and $\boldsymbol{b}$, and C is the mid point of AB. Find in terms of $\boldsymbol{a}$ and $\boldsymbol{b}$ the vectors $\overrightarrow{AC}$ and $\overrightarrow{OC}$.

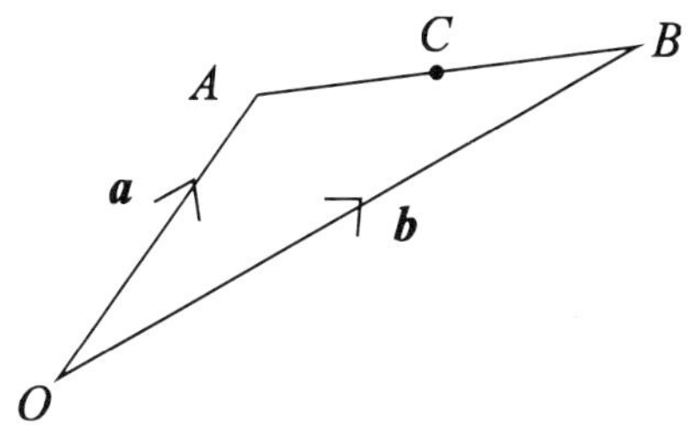

From the definition of multiplication by a scalar

$$\overrightarrow{AC} = \frac{1}{2}\overrightarrow{AB} = \frac{1}{2}(\boldsymbol{b} - \boldsymbol{a}).$$

The addition law gives

$$\overrightarrow{OC} = \overrightarrow{OA} + \overrightarrow{AC} = \boldsymbol{a} + \frac{1}{2}(\boldsymbol{b} - \boldsymbol{a}) = \frac{1}{2}(\boldsymbol{b} + \boldsymbol{a}).$$

Example 5.2.

The vectors $\boldsymbol{p}$ and $\boldsymbol{q}$ are defined by $\boldsymbol{p} = 2\boldsymbol{a} + 3\boldsymbol{b}$, $\boldsymbol{q} = 4\boldsymbol{a} + 5\boldsymbol{b}$. Express, in terms of $\boldsymbol{a}$ and $\boldsymbol{b}$, (a) $\boldsymbol{p} + 3\boldsymbol{q}$, (b) $2\boldsymbol{p} - \boldsymbol{q}$, (c) the vector $\boldsymbol{c}$ such that $3\boldsymbol{p} + \boldsymbol{q} + \boldsymbol{c} = \boldsymbol{a}$.

(a) Substituting for $\boldsymbol{p}$ and $\boldsymbol{q}$ in $\boldsymbol{p} + 3\boldsymbol{q}$ gives

$$\boldsymbol{p} + 3\boldsymbol{q} = 2\boldsymbol{a} + 3\boldsymbol{b} + 3(4\boldsymbol{a} + 5\boldsymbol{b})$$
$$= 2\boldsymbol{a} + 3\boldsymbol{b} + 12\boldsymbol{a} + 15\boldsymbol{b} = 14\boldsymbol{a} + 18\boldsymbol{b}.$$

(b) Similarly

$$2\boldsymbol{p} - \boldsymbol{q} = 2(2\boldsymbol{a} + 3\boldsymbol{b}) - (4\boldsymbol{a} + 5\boldsymbol{b}) = \boldsymbol{b}.$$

(c) Substituting for $\boldsymbol{p}$ and $\boldsymbol{q}$ in $3\boldsymbol{p} + \boldsymbol{q} + \boldsymbol{c}$ gives

$$3\boldsymbol{p} + \boldsymbol{q} + \boldsymbol{c} = 3(2\boldsymbol{a} + 3\boldsymbol{b}) + (4\boldsymbol{a} + 5\boldsymbol{b}) + \boldsymbol{c} = 10\boldsymbol{a} + 14\boldsymbol{b} + \boldsymbol{c}.$$

Equating this to $\boldsymbol{a}$ gives

$$10\boldsymbol{a} + 14\boldsymbol{b} + \boldsymbol{c} = \boldsymbol{a},$$

so that

$$\boldsymbol{c} = -9\boldsymbol{a} - 14\boldsymbol{b}.$$

Example 5.3

In the diagram the vector $\boldsymbol{a}$ is of length 2 and makes an acute angle of 45° with the dotted line shown and the vector $\boldsymbol{b}$ is of length 3 and makes an acute angle of 60° with the dotted line. Find the magnitude and direction of $2\boldsymbol{a} + 3\boldsymbol{b}$.

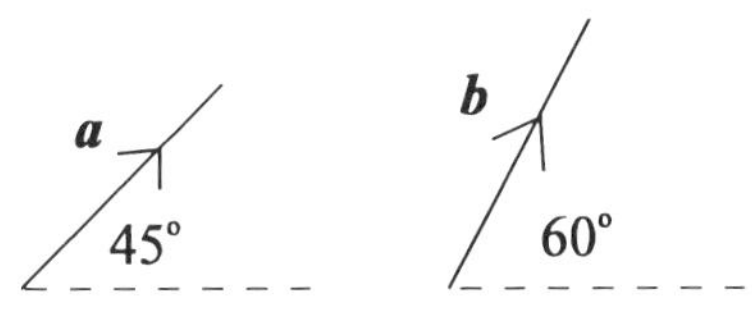

In the following diagram $\overrightarrow{OA}$ represents the vector $2\boldsymbol{a}$ and is therefore of length 4, $\overrightarrow{AB}$ represents the vector $3\boldsymbol{b}$ and is therefore of length 9. The angle OAB is 165°.

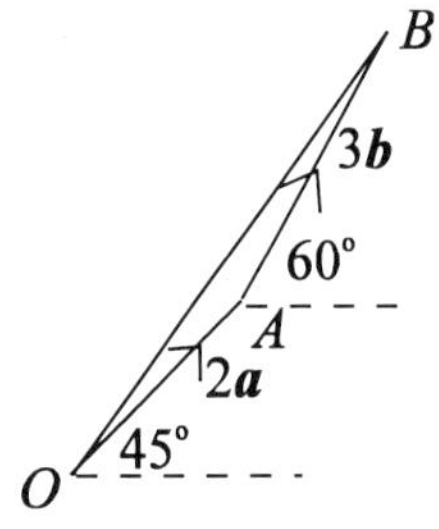

$\overrightarrow{OB}$ represents $2\boldsymbol{a} + 3\boldsymbol{b}$ and applying the cosine rule to triangle OAB gives

$$OB^2 = 4^2 + 9^2 - 2 \times 4 \times 9 \times \cos 165°,$$

and therefore $$OB = 12.91.$$

Applying the sine rule to triangle OAB gives

$$\frac{\sin B\hat{O}A}{9} = \frac{\sin 165^{\circ}}{OB},$$

giving angle $B\hat{O}A = 10.4°$. Therefore $2\boldsymbol{a} + 3\boldsymbol{b}$ is of magnitude 12.91 at an angle of 55.4° to the dotted line.

This is not really the quickest way of finding $2\boldsymbol{a} + 3\boldsymbol{b}$ and the alternative method using components and described in the following section is more efficient.

Exercises 5.1

1

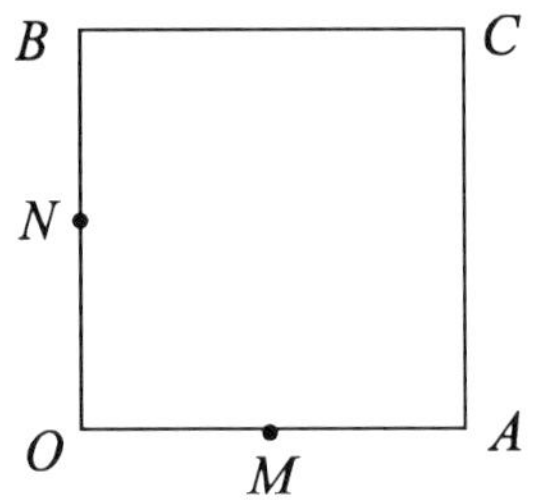

In the square $OACB$ the midpoint of OA is M and the midpoint of OB is N. The vectors $\overrightarrow{OA}$ and $\overrightarrow{OB}$ are denoted by $\boldsymbol{a}$ and $\boldsymbol{b}$, respectively. Express in terms of $\boldsymbol{a}$ and $\boldsymbol{b}$ (a) $\overrightarrow{OM}$, (b) $\overrightarrow{NO}$, (c) $\overrightarrow{AB}$, (d) $\overrightarrow{AC}$, (e) $\overrightarrow{BA}$, (f) $\overrightarrow{MN}$.

2

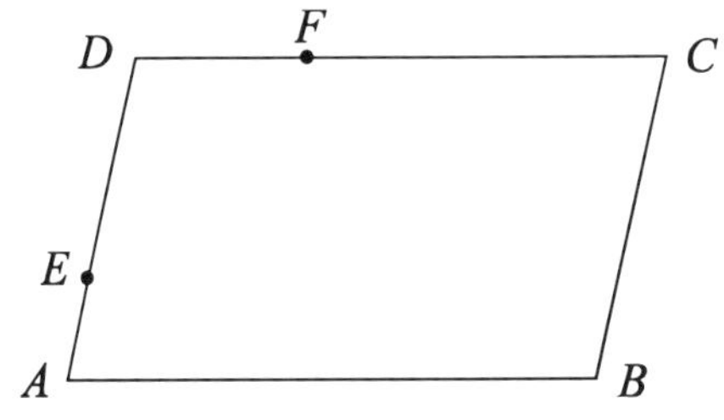

In the parallelogram $ABCD$, E is the point on AD where $AE = \frac{1}{3}AD$ and F is the point on DC where $DF = \frac{1}{3}DC$. The vectors $\overrightarrow{\boldsymbol{AB}}$ and $\overrightarrow{\boldsymbol{AD}}$ are denoted by $\boldsymbol{a}$ and $\boldsymbol{b}$, respectively.

Express in terms of $\boldsymbol{a}$ and $\boldsymbol{b}$ (a) $\overrightarrow{\boldsymbol{DF}}$, (b) $\overrightarrow{\boldsymbol{AC}}$, (c) $\overrightarrow{\boldsymbol{AF}}$, (d) $\overrightarrow{\boldsymbol{CF}}$, (e) $\overrightarrow{\boldsymbol{EF}}$.

3

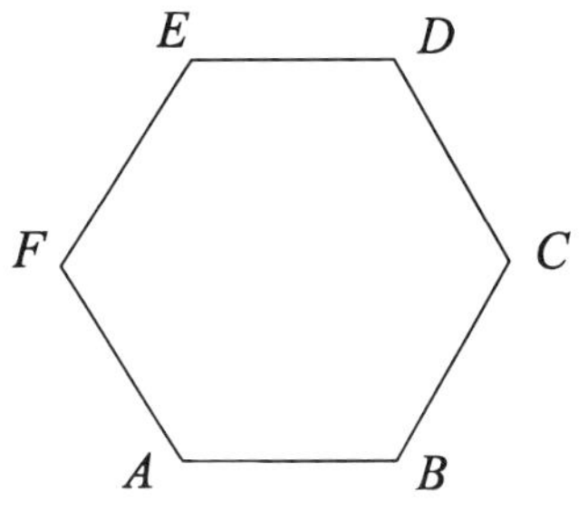

In the regular hexagon $ABCDEF$ the vectors $\overrightarrow{\boldsymbol{AB}}$ and $\overrightarrow{\boldsymbol{BC}}$ are denoted by $\boldsymbol{a}$ and $\boldsymbol{b}$, respectively. Show that $\overrightarrow{\boldsymbol{CD}} = \boldsymbol{b} - \boldsymbol{a}$ and express (a) $\overrightarrow{\boldsymbol{DE}}$, (b) $\overrightarrow{\boldsymbol{EF}}$, (c) $\overrightarrow{\boldsymbol{FA}}$ in terms of $\boldsymbol{a}$ and $\boldsymbol{b}$. The points P and Q lie on BC and FE, respectively, with $BP = \frac{1}{4}BC$ and $FQ = \frac{1}{5}FE$.

Express $\overrightarrow{\boldsymbol{PQ}}$ in terms of $\boldsymbol{a}$ and $\boldsymbol{b}$.

4 The vectors $\boldsymbol{p}$ and $\boldsymbol{q}$ are defined by $\boldsymbol{p} = 4\boldsymbol{a} + 6\boldsymbol{b}$, $\boldsymbol{q} = 2\boldsymbol{a} - 5\boldsymbol{b}$.

Express, in terms of $\boldsymbol{a}$ and $\boldsymbol{b}$, (a) $2\boldsymbol{p} + 4\boldsymbol{q}$, (b) $3\boldsymbol{p} - 4\boldsymbol{q}$,

(c) the vector $\boldsymbol{c}$ such that $2\boldsymbol{p} + 5\boldsymbol{q} + \boldsymbol{c} = 2\boldsymbol{a} + 5\boldsymbol{b}$.

5

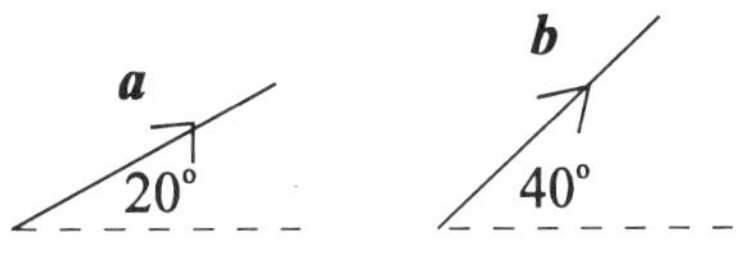

In the diagram the vector $\boldsymbol{a}$ is of length 3 and makes an acute angle of 20° with the dotted line shown and the vector $\boldsymbol{b}$ is of length 4 and makes an acute angle of 40° with the dotted line.

Find the magnitude and direction of (a) $\boldsymbol{a} + \boldsymbol{b}$, (b) $3\boldsymbol{a} + 4\boldsymbol{b}$.

5.3 Vectors in two dimensions

The basic ideas involved with vectors are the same in two and three dimensions but, in order to get used to them, it is better to start with the slightly simpler case of two dimensions.

Cartesian components (or resolutes)

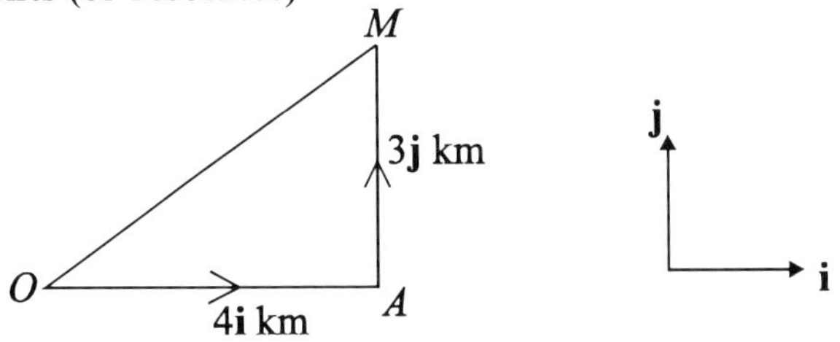

The diagram shows the final position of a man M who has travelled 4 km east from a point O to a point A and then travelled 3 km directly north from A. His final displacement is the vector sum of his displacements east and north i.e.

$$\overrightarrow{OM} = \overrightarrow{OA} + \overrightarrow{AM}.$$

Unit vectors **i** and **j** can be chosen so that **i** points to the east and **j** points north. Perpendicular unit vectors like these are generally called cartesian unit vectors. Then $\overrightarrow{OA} = OA\,\mathbf{i} = 4\,\mathbf{i}$ km and $\overrightarrow{AM} = AM\,\mathbf{j} = 3\,\mathbf{j}$ km and

$$\overrightarrow{OM} = (OA\,\mathbf{i} + AM\,\mathbf{j}) = (4\,\mathbf{i} + 3\,\mathbf{j})\text{ km}.$$

This alternative form of the displacement is called its cartesian component form and it is the most useful form for a vector. The lengths of OA and AM, i.e. the numbers 4 and 3, are the cartesian components (or resolutes), in metres, of the displacement in the direction of **i** and **j** respectively. The adjective cartesian will, for brevity, normally be omitted in subsequent work.

Any two dimensional vector can be expressed in the form $c\,\mathbf{i} + d\,\mathbf{j}$, the coefficients c and d of **i** and **j**, respectively, are called the components in the **i** and **j** directions, respectively.

The components are not always positive. This can be seen from the diagram

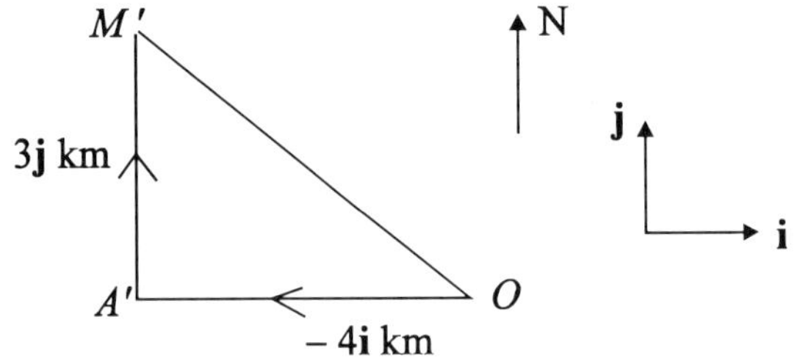

which shows the position M' of the man after travelling west a distance of 4 km to the point A' and then 3 km North from A'. In this case

$$\overrightarrow{OM'} = \overrightarrow{OA'} + \overrightarrow{A'M'},$$

however $\overrightarrow{OA'}$ is in the opposite direction to **i** and therefore

$$\overrightarrow{OA'} = -4\,\mathbf{i}\text{ km and }\overrightarrow{A'M'} = 3\,\mathbf{j}\text{ km so that}$$

$$\overrightarrow{OM'} = (-4\,\mathbf{i} + 3\,\mathbf{j})\text{ km},$$

showing the possibility of a negative component.

The length OM, i.e. the magnitude of the vector $\overrightarrow{OM}$ is, by Pythagoras' Theorem, 5 km. This is the square root of the sums of the squares of the components and is the definition of the magnitude of a vector in cartesian component form.
The **i, j** notation is the one generally used in mechanics but an entirely equivalent representation is possible using column vectors when

$$\overrightarrow{OM} = \begin{pmatrix} 4 \\ 3 \end{pmatrix} \text{ km, and } \overrightarrow{OM'} = \begin{pmatrix} -4 \\ 3 \end{pmatrix} \text{ km.}$$

Components of a position vector

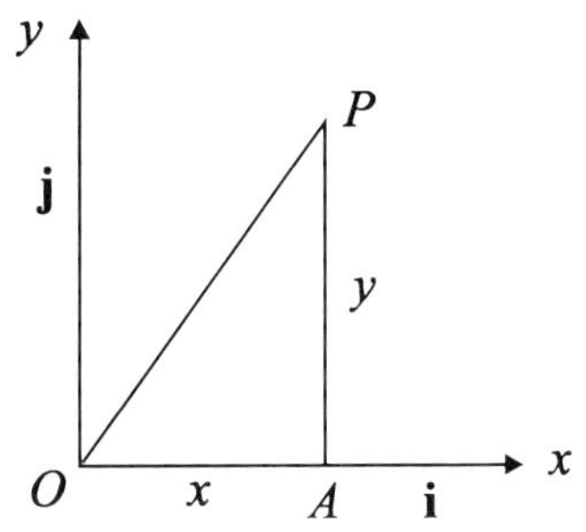

In the diagram **i** and **j** denote unit vectors along the Ox and Oy axes. The perpendicular from the point P (x, y) to the x axis intersects it at the point A. Therefore $\overrightarrow{OA} = x\,\mathbf{i}$, $\overrightarrow{AP} = y\,\mathbf{j}$, and $\overrightarrow{OP} = \overrightarrow{OA} + \overrightarrow{AP} = x\,\mathbf{i} + y\,\mathbf{j}$. Also $\overrightarrow{OP}$, the position vector of the point P is usually denoted by $\boldsymbol{r}$ so that

$$\boldsymbol{r} = x\,\mathbf{i} + y\,\mathbf{j},$$

and

$$|\,\boldsymbol{r}\,| = r = \sqrt{x^2 + y^2}\ .$$

<u>**Example 5.4**</u>
Find the position vectors of the points with cartesian coordinates (4, 6) and (−4, 3).

The components of the position vectors are the coordinates and therefore the required vectors are 4**i** + 6**j** and −4**i** + 3**j** and have magnitudes $\sqrt{52}$ and $\sqrt{25} = 5$, respectively.

The following summarises the properties of a vector when expressed in cartesian component form.

Equality of vectors
Vectors are equal if and only if all their components are equal.

Example 5.5

Given that the vectors $\boldsymbol{a} = (4 - x)\,\mathbf{i} + 6\,\mathbf{j}$ and $\boldsymbol{b} = 7\,\mathbf{i} + (5 - y)\,\mathbf{j}$ are equal, find x and y.

It is given that

$$\boldsymbol{a} = (4 - x)\,\mathbf{i} + 6\,\mathbf{j} = \boldsymbol{b} = 7\,\mathbf{i} + (5 - y)\,\mathbf{j},$$

the vectors can only be equal if their components are equal i.e.

$$4 - x = 7, \qquad 6 = 5 - y,$$

therefore $x = -3$ and $y = -1$.

Negative vectors

If $\boldsymbol{a} = c\,\mathbf{i} + d\,\mathbf{j}$ then $-\boldsymbol{a} = -c\,\mathbf{i} - d\,\mathbf{j}$,

i.e. the signs of both components are changed.

Multiplication by a scalar

If $\boldsymbol{a} = c\,\mathbf{i} + d\,\mathbf{j}$ then $m\,\boldsymbol{a} = mc\,\mathbf{i} + md\,\mathbf{j}$,

i.e. both components are multiplied by m.

Addition and subtraction of vectors

The sum or difference of one or more vectors is the vector whose components are the sums or differences of the corresponding components of the two vectors.

Example 5.6

The vectors $\boldsymbol{p}$ and $\boldsymbol{q}$ are given by $\boldsymbol{p} = 2\mathbf{i} + 8\mathbf{j}$, $\boldsymbol{q} = 5\mathbf{i} - 3\mathbf{j}$. Find, in cartesian component form, (a) $\boldsymbol{p} + \boldsymbol{q}$, (b) $2\boldsymbol{p} + 4\boldsymbol{q}$, (c) $3\boldsymbol{p} - 2\boldsymbol{q}$.

(a) $\quad \boldsymbol{p} + \boldsymbol{q} = 2\mathbf{i} + 8\mathbf{j} + 5\mathbf{i} - 3\mathbf{j} = 7\mathbf{i} + 5\mathbf{j}$.

(b) $\quad 2\boldsymbol{p} + 4\boldsymbol{q} = 2(2\mathbf{i} + 8\mathbf{j}) + 4(5\mathbf{i} - 3\mathbf{j}) = 24\mathbf{i} + 4\mathbf{j}$.

(c) $\quad 3\boldsymbol{p} - 2\boldsymbol{q} = 3(2\mathbf{i} + 8\mathbf{j}) - 2(5\mathbf{i} - 3\mathbf{j}) = -4\mathbf{i} + 30\mathbf{j}$.

Zero vector

This is the vector with zero components and is denoted usually by $\boldsymbol{0}$. The rule for the subtraction of two vectors shows that

$$\boldsymbol{a} - \boldsymbol{a} = \boldsymbol{0}.$$

Vector joining two points

If $\boldsymbol{a}$ and $\boldsymbol{b}$ are the position vectors of two points A and B then it was shown on page 86 that $\overrightarrow{AB} = \boldsymbol{b} - \boldsymbol{a}$. The components of $\boldsymbol{a}$ and $\boldsymbol{b}$ are the coordinates of the corresponding points. Therefore the rule for subtraction shows that the components of the vector joining two points are the differences in the corresponding coordinates of the points.

Example 5.7

Find the vector $\overrightarrow{PQ}$ where the coordinates of P and Q are (2, 1) and (5, −3) respectively.

The position vectors $\boldsymbol{p}$ and $\boldsymbol{q}$ of P and Q are $\boldsymbol{p} = 2\mathbf{i} + \mathbf{j}$ and $\boldsymbol{q} = 5\mathbf{i} - 3\mathbf{j}$.
Also $\overrightarrow{PQ} = \boldsymbol{q} - \boldsymbol{p} = 5\mathbf{i} - 3\mathbf{j} - (2\mathbf{i} + \mathbf{j}) = 3\mathbf{i} - 4\mathbf{j}$.

Magnitude of a vector

The magnitude of the vector $c\,\mathbf{i} + d\,\mathbf{j}$ is $\sqrt{c^2 + d^2}$ i.e. the magnitude is the square root of the sum of the squares of the components.

Example 5.8

Find the magnitudes of the vectors (a) $3\mathbf{i} + 4\mathbf{j}$, (b) $7\mathbf{i} - 11\mathbf{j}$.

The magnitude of a vector is the square root of the sum of the squares of the components. Therefore for (a) the magnitude is $\sqrt{3^2 + 4^2} = 5$ and for (b) the magnitude is

$$\sqrt{7^2 + (-11)^2} = 13.04.$$

Example 5.9

Find the vector in the direction of the vector $5\mathbf{i} + 12\mathbf{j}$ and of magnitude 104.

The required vector is $k(5\mathbf{i} + 12\mathbf{j})$, where k is a constant. The magnitude of the vector is $k\sqrt{5^2 + 12^2} = 13k = 104$ so that $k = 8$ giving the required vector as $40\mathbf{i} + 96\mathbf{j}$.

Unit vectors

The unit vector in the direction of the vector $\boldsymbol{a} = c\,\mathbf{i} + d\,\mathbf{j}$ is $\dfrac{c\mathbf{i} + d\mathbf{j}}{\sqrt{c^2 + d^2}}$.

Example 5.10

Find the unit vectors in the direction of the vectors (a) $3\mathbf{i} - 4\mathbf{j}$, and (b) $4\mathbf{i} + 7\mathbf{j}$.

(a) The unit vector is found by dividing the vector by its magnitude.
The magnitude is $\sqrt{3^2 + 4^2} = 5$
and therefore the unit vector is $\dfrac{3\mathbf{i} - 4\mathbf{j}}{5} = 0.6\mathbf{i} - 0.8\mathbf{j}$.

(b) In this case the magnitude of the vector is $\sqrt{4^2 + 7^2} = \sqrt{65}$
and the unit vector is $\dfrac{4\mathbf{i} + 7\mathbf{j}}{\sqrt{65}}$.

Conversion to cartesian component form

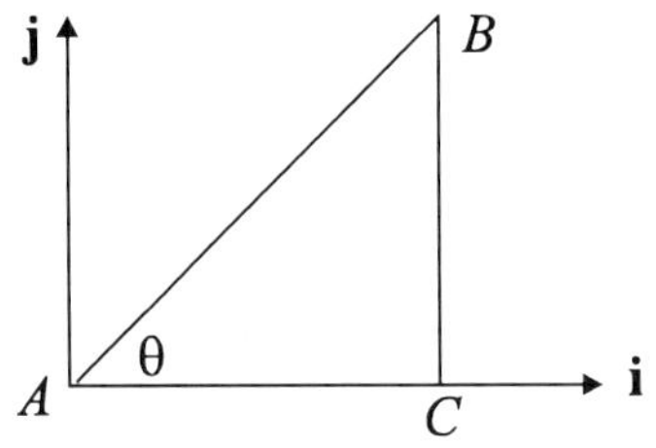

In the above diagram $\overrightarrow{AB}$ represents the vector $\boldsymbol{a}$ and lines AC and CB are drawn parallel to the cartesian unit vectors **i** and **j**. The vectors $\overrightarrow{AC}$ and $\overrightarrow{CB}$ are therefore $AC\,\mathbf{i}$ and $CB\,\mathbf{j}$, respectively, and the law of vector addition gives $\overrightarrow{AB} = AC\,\mathbf{i} + CB\,\mathbf{j}$. The cartesian component (i.e. resolute) of $\overrightarrow{AB}$ in the direction of **i** is therefore AC, which is equal to $AB \cos \theta$, where θ is the angle between $\overrightarrow{AB}$ and **i**. Similarly the cartesian component (i.e. resolute) of $\overrightarrow{AB}$ in the direction of **j** is therefore BC, which is equal to $AB \sin \theta$.

There is a current practice that the adjective cartesian is usually dropped and the component (i.e. resolute) of a vector in any direction is defined to be the product of the magnitude of the vector and the cosine of the angle between the vector and the chosen direction. You have already met this with forces in M1. This definition is obviously not valid when the component directions are not perpendicular. Therefore if the word component is used then, unless there is evidence to the contrary, it should be interpreted as the cartesian component or resolute.

In calculating the component form you have to be careful, as in Statics, to pick the correct angle and take its cosine correctly. You could also resolve a vector first into two positive components along the lines containing **i** and **j** and then adjust the signs.

It is often helpful when doing theoretical work with vectors to label the components so that it is immediately obvious which is the **i** component and which is the **j** component. Since these unit vectors are usually taken to be parallel to the x and y axes, respectively, one method of identifying the components is to use a suffix notation i.e. the **i** and **j** components of the vector $\boldsymbol{a}$ are denoted by a_x and a_y, respectively, so that $\boldsymbol{a} = a_x\,\mathbf{i} + a_y\,\mathbf{j}$. This notation will be used from now on. Another notation which is sometimes used is a numerical one with the **i** and **j** components of the vector $\boldsymbol{a}$ being denoted by a_1 and a_2 respectively.

Conversion from component form

If a vector $\boldsymbol{a}$ is represented by $\overrightarrow{OA}$ then the above argument shows that the components a_x and a_y are given by

$$a_x = OA \cos \theta, \qquad a_y = OA \sin \theta$$

Squaring and adding gives

$$OA = \sqrt{a_x^{\,2} + a_y^{\,2}}\ .$$

You can then find cos θ (sin θ) and the signs of a_x and a_y will tell you in which quadrant the vector lies and you can then find θ.

Example 5.11 (This is effectively Example 5.3 repeated)

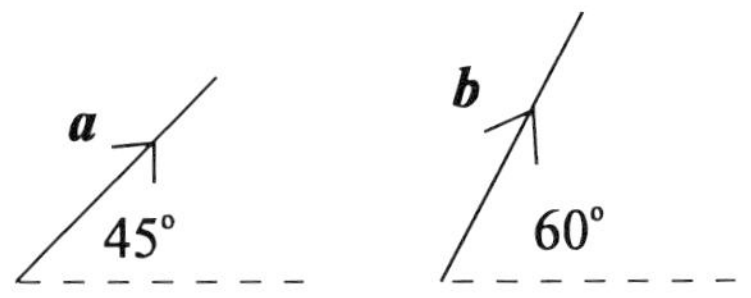

In the diagram the vector ***a*** is of length 2 and makes an acute angle of 45° with the unit vector **i** and the vector ***b*** is of length 3 and makes an acute angle of 60° with **j.** Convert the vectors ***a*** and ***b*** to cartesian component form and find the cartesion component form of 2**a** + 3***b***. Find also the magnitude and direction of 2**a** + 3***b***.

The components of ***a*** in the direction of **i** and **j** are 2 cos 45° and 2 sin 45° respectively.
Therefore ***a*** = $\sqrt{2}$ **i** + $\sqrt{2}$ **j.**
The components of ***b*** in the direction of **i** and **j** are 3 cos 60° and 3 sin 60° respectively.

Therefore $\quad \boldsymbol{b} = \frac{3}{2}\mathbf{i} + \frac{3\sqrt{3}}{2}\mathbf{j}.$

Therefore $2\boldsymbol{a} + 3\,\boldsymbol{b} = 2(\sqrt{2}\,\mathrm{i} + \sqrt{2}\,\mathrm{j}) + 3(\frac{3}{2}\mathbf{i} + \frac{3\sqrt{3}}{2}\mathbf{j}) = 7.33\,\mathbf{i} + 10.62\,\mathbf{j}$.

The magnitude of the vector is 12.91 and it makes an angle $\tan^{-1}\dfrac{10.62}{7.33} = 55.4°$ with **i.**

These are the same results as obtained in Example 5.3.

Exercises 5.2

1 Find x and y in each of the following cases
   (a) when ***a*** = (5 – *x*)**i** + 3**j**, ***b*** = 9**i** + (4 – *y*)**j** and ***a* = *b***
   (b) when ***a*** = (3 – *x*)**i** + 4**j,** ***b*** = 2**i** + (7 – *y*)**j** and ***a*** = 2***b***,
   (c) when ***a*** = (5 – *x* – *y*)**i** + (3 – *x*)**j,** ***b*** = 4**i** + (6 – *y*)**j** and 2***a*** = **-*b*.**

2 Given that ***a*** **= 2i** + 8**j,** ***b*** = –3**i** + 5**j,** ***c*** = 5**i** – 3**j** find (a) 2***a*** + 3***b***, (b) 5***b*** – 2***a***, (c) 2***a*** + 4***b*** + ***c*,** (d) ***a*** – 3***b*** + 2***c*.**

3 Find the position vectors of the following points *P* (1,4), *Q* (3, -2), *R* (–4,3), *S* (–2, –6).

4 Find, for the points in the previous exercise, $\overrightarrow{PQ}$, $\overrightarrow{RS}$, $\overrightarrow{PS}$, $\overrightarrow{QR}$, $\overrightarrow{PR}$.

5 Find the magnitudes of the following vectors and the unit vectors along them.
(a) $5\mathbf{i} + 12\mathbf{j}$, (b) $2\mathbf{i} - 7\mathbf{j}$, (c) $-3\mathbf{i}+6\mathbf{j}$, (d) $-4\mathbf{i} - 6\mathbf{j}$.

6 In the following, d denotes the magnitude of a vector and θ denotes the angle it makes with the positive x axis (i.e. the unit vector **i**). Find the cartesian component form of each vector.
(a) $d = 4$, $\theta = 60^\circ$ (b) $d = 6$, $\theta = 150^\circ$, (c) $d = 10$, $\theta = 200^\circ$, (d) $d = 3$, $\theta = -40^\circ$

7 Find the magnitude and direction of the following vectors.
(a) $3\mathbf{i} + 7\mathbf{j}$, (b) $4\mathbf{i} - 6\mathbf{j}$ (c) $-2\mathbf{i} + 5\mathbf{j}$, (d) $-8\mathbf{i} - 4\mathbf{j}$.

8 Unit vectors **i** and **j** are defined to be East and North respectively. Give the following displacements in cartesian component form (a) 50 km, bearing 060°, (b) 80 km, bearing 120°, (c) 100 km, bearing 225°, (d) 75 km, bearing 300°.

5.4 Vectors in three dimensions

So far you have only come across displacements which are all in the same plane (i.e. the same flat surface) and therefore cannot be expressed in terms of two perpendicular directions. Not all displacements can be expressed in this way, for example, the position of a moving object, such as an aircraft, will not stay for long in the same plane. It is therefore necessary to extend the idea of components to three dimensions.

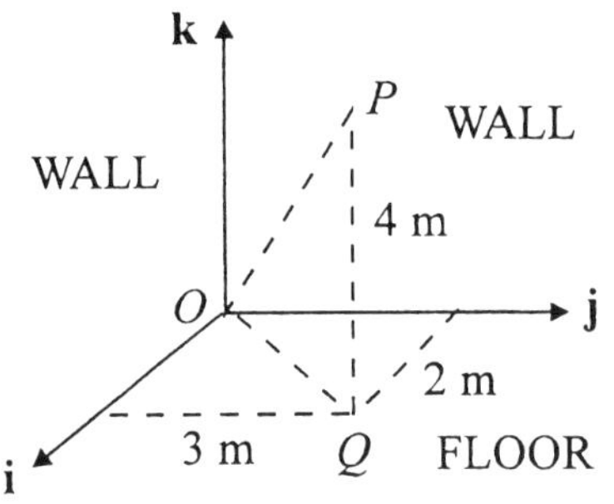

You can imagine how to do this by trying to see how to fix the position of a point in a room, with vertical walls and a horizontal floor. Any point on the floor is determined by its distances from two adjacent walls. If unit vectors **i** and **j** are taken along two adjacent edges, then the displacement $\overrightarrow{OQ}$ of the point Q which is at a distance of 2 m from one wall and 3 m from the adjacent wall is $(2\mathbf{i} + 3\mathbf{j})$ m. In order to determine the displacement of the point P a distance of 4m directly above Q, a third unit vector **k** vertically upwards has to be introduced as shown in the diagram. The unit vectors **i**, **j** and **k** are therefore parallel to the edges of the floor and up the wall at the corner O.

The displacement $\overrightarrow{QP}$ is therefore 4 **k** m and applying the law of vector addition to the triangle *OQP* gives

$$\overrightarrow{OP} = \overrightarrow{OQ} + \overrightarrow{QP}$$

i.e.
$$\overrightarrow{OP} = (2\mathbf{i} + 3\mathbf{j} + 4\mathbf{k})\text{ m.}$$

This is the representation of the displacement vector in cartesian component form and, in general, any vector has such a representation.
It follows from Pythagoras' Theorem that

$$OP^2 = OQ^2 + PQ^2 = 2^2 + 3^2 + 4^2$$

so that the magnitude is the square root of the sum of the squares of the components.

The displacement $\overrightarrow{OP}$ is given in the column vector notation by

$$\overrightarrow{OP} = \begin{pmatrix} 2 \\ 3 \\ 4 \end{pmatrix} \text{ m .}$$

The unit vectors **i**, **j** and **k** are mutually perpendicular vectors (i.e. each one of them is perpendicular to the other two, this can be seen from the above diagram for a corner of a room. The three directions can also be visualised by putting out your thumb and two adjacent figures on the right hand so that each one is perpendicular to the other two as shown in the diagram.

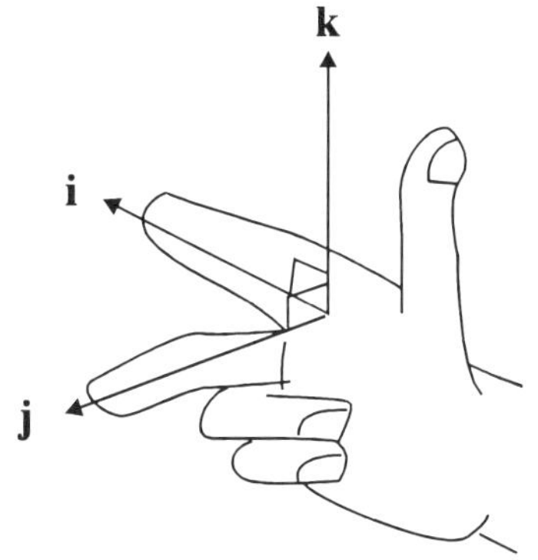

The first finger is in the direction of **i**, the second finger is in the direction of **j** and the thumb is in the direction of **k**. The particular directions shown in the diagram have the additional property that they are what is called right handed. This means that if you imagine a rotation of a screw in the sense from **i** to **j** then it will move in the direction of **k**.

Components of position vector

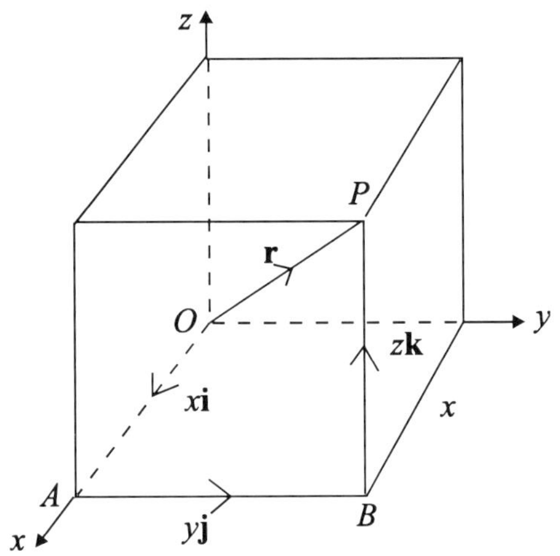

In the diagram three mutually perpendicular axes Ox, Oy and Oz are shown. These are like the three intersecting lines at the corner of a room. The perpendicular displacement of the point P from the plane containing Oy and Oz is denoted by x and this plane is called the plane $x = 0$. Similarly the perpendicular displacements of the point P from the plane containing Ox and Oz and the plane containing Ox and Oy are denoted by y and z, respectively, with the planes being referred to as the planes $y = 0$ and $z = 0$ respectively. These three numbers are the cartesian co-ordinates of P and determine it uniquely. In the above example of a point in a room $x = 2$, $y = 3$ and $z = 4$. The unit vectors **i**, **j** and **k** are defined to be along the axes Ox, Oy and Oz respectively. The displacement $\overrightarrow{OP}$ is the sum of the displacements $\overrightarrow{OA}$, $\overrightarrow{AB}$ and $\overrightarrow{BP}$ shown in the diagram. Also

$$\overrightarrow{OA} = x\,\mathbf{i},\ \overrightarrow{AB} = y\,\mathbf{j} \text{ and } \overrightarrow{BP} = z\,\mathbf{k}.$$

Therefore, $\boldsymbol{r}$, the position vector of the point P, is given by

$$\boldsymbol{r} = x\,\mathbf{i} + y\,\mathbf{j} + z\,\mathbf{k}.$$

Since the unit vectors **i, j** and **k** are generally taken along the axes Ox, Oy and Oz the suffix notation introduced earlier is often used to denote the components in these directions i.e. a vector $\boldsymbol{a}$ is often written as

$$\boldsymbol{a} = a_x\,\mathbf{i} + a_y\,\mathbf{j} + a_z\,\mathbf{k},$$

or, in column vector notation, as $\boldsymbol{a} = \begin{pmatrix} a_x \\ a_y \\ a_z \end{pmatrix}$

The same basic rules for vectors hold in three dimensions as in two dimensions i.e.

(i) Vectors are equal if, and only if, all their components are equal.

(ii) If $\boldsymbol{a} = a_x\,\mathbf{i} + a_y\,\mathbf{j} + a_z\,\mathbf{k}$ then $-\boldsymbol{a} = -a_x\,\mathbf{i} - a_y\,\mathbf{j} - a_z\,\mathbf{k}$.

(iii) The sum (difference) of one or more vectors is the vector whose components are the sums (differences) of the corresponding components.

(iv) The components of the vector joining two points is the difference in the co-ordinates of the points.

(v) Multiplying a vector by a scalar means that each component is multiplied by the scalar.

(vi) The magnitude of a vector $\boldsymbol{a} = a_x\,\mathbf{i} + a_y\,\mathbf{j} + a_z\,\mathbf{k}$ is $\sqrt{a_x^2 + a_y^2 + a_z^2}$.

(vii) The unit vector in the direction of $\boldsymbol{a}$ is $\dfrac{a_x\mathbf{i} + a_y\mathbf{j} + a_z\mathbf{k}}{\sqrt{a_x^2 + a_y^2 + a_z^2}}$.

Problems involving three dimensional vectors in cartesian form can be handled exactly as those in two dimensions, the only difference being that there are now three components to consider!

Example 5.12

Given that the vectors $\boldsymbol{a} = (2 - x)\,\mathbf{i} + 4\,\mathbf{j} + 8\,\mathbf{k}$ and $\mathbf{b} = 7\,\mathbf{i} + (5 - y)\,\mathbf{j} + 4z\,\mathbf{k}$ are equal, find x, y and z.

Since the vectors are equal their components are also equal and therefore

$$2 - x = 7,\ 4 = 5 - y,\ 8 = 4z.$$

solving these gives $x = -5$, $y = 1$, $z = 2$.

Example 5.13

Find the position vectors of the points with cartesian co-ordinates (3, 1, 5) and (−5, 2, 3).

The components of the position vectors are the co-ordinates and therefore the required vectors are $3\mathbf{i} + \mathbf{j} + 5\mathbf{k}$ and $-5\mathbf{i} + 2\mathbf{j} + 3\mathbf{k}$.

Example 5.14

The vectors $\boldsymbol{p}$ and $\boldsymbol{q}$ are given by $\boldsymbol{p} = 3\mathbf{i} + 5\mathbf{j} + 2\mathbf{k}$, $\boldsymbol{q} = 5\mathbf{i} - 3\mathbf{j} + 7\mathbf{k}$. Find (a) $2\boldsymbol{p} + \boldsymbol{q}$, (b) $\boldsymbol{p} + 3\boldsymbol{q}$, (c) $3\boldsymbol{p} - 2\boldsymbol{q}$.

(a) $2\boldsymbol{p} + \boldsymbol{q} = 2(3\mathbf{i} + 5\mathbf{j} + 2\mathbf{k}) + 5\mathbf{i} - 3\mathbf{j} + 7\mathbf{k} = 11\mathbf{i} + 7\mathbf{j} + 11\mathbf{k}$.

(b) $\boldsymbol{p} + 3\boldsymbol{q} = (3\mathbf{i} + 5\mathbf{j} + 2\mathbf{k}) + 3(5\mathbf{i} - 3\mathbf{j} + 7\mathbf{k}) = 18\mathbf{i} - 4\mathbf{j} + 23\mathbf{k}$.

(c) $3\boldsymbol{p} - 2\boldsymbol{q} = 3(3\mathbf{i} + 5\mathbf{j} + 2\mathbf{k}) - 2(5\mathbf{i} - 3\mathbf{j} + 7\mathbf{k}) = -\mathbf{i} + 21\mathbf{j} - 8\mathbf{k}$.

Example 5.15

Find the magnitudes of the vectors (a) $2\mathbf{i} - \mathbf{j} + 2\mathbf{k}$, (b) $4\mathbf{i} - 2\mathbf{j} + 9\mathbf{k}$.

The magnitude of a vector is the square root of the sum of the squares of the components. Therefore for (a) the magnitude is $\sqrt{2^2 + (-1)^2 + 2^2} = 3$ and for (b) the magnitude is $\sqrt{4^2 + (-2)^2 + 9^2} = 10.04$.

Example 5.16

Find the vector $\overrightarrow{PQ}$ where the co-ordinates of P and Q are (4, 1, 6) and (5, −9, 3) respectively.

The position vectors $\boldsymbol{p}$ and $\boldsymbol{q}$ of P and Q are $\boldsymbol{p} = 4\mathbf{i} + \mathbf{j} + 6\mathbf{k}$ and $\boldsymbol{q} = 5\mathbf{i} - 9\mathbf{j} + 3\mathbf{k}$.
Also $\overrightarrow{PQ} = \boldsymbol{q} - \boldsymbol{p} = 5\mathbf{i} - 9\mathbf{j} + 3\mathbf{k} - (4\mathbf{i} + \mathbf{j} + 6\mathbf{k}) = \mathbf{i} - 10\,\mathbf{j} - 3\mathbf{k}$.

Example 5.17

Find the unit vectors in the direction of the vectors (a) $2\mathbf{i} + \mathbf{j} - 2\mathbf{k}$ and (b) $5\mathbf{i} - 3\mathbf{j} + 7\mathbf{k}$.

(a) The unit vector is found by dividing the vector by its magnitude. The magnitude is $\sqrt{2^2 + 1^2 + (-2)^2} = 3$ and therefore the unit vector is $\dfrac{2\mathbf{i} + \mathbf{j} - 2\mathbf{k}}{3}$.

(b) In this case the magnitude of the vector is $\sqrt{5^2 + (-3)^2 + 7^2} = \sqrt{83}$ and the unit vector is $\dfrac{5\mathbf{i} - 3\mathbf{j} + 7\mathbf{k}}{\sqrt{83}}$.

Exercises 5.3

1 Find x, y and z in each of the following cases
 (a) when $\boldsymbol{a} = (7 - x)\,\mathbf{i} + 4\mathbf{j} + 3\mathbf{k}$, $\boldsymbol{b} = 9\mathbf{i} + (4 - y)\,\mathbf{j} + (2 - z)\,\mathbf{k}$ and $\boldsymbol{a} = \boldsymbol{b}$,
 (b) when $\boldsymbol{a} = (4 + x)\,\mathbf{i} + 11\mathbf{j} + 5\mathbf{k}$, $\boldsymbol{b} = 3\,\mathbf{i} + (8 - y)\,\mathbf{j} + (7 + 2z)\,\mathbf{k}$ and $\boldsymbol{a} = 2\boldsymbol{b}$,
 (c) when $\boldsymbol{a} = (9 - x - y)\,\mathbf{i} + (2 - x)\,\mathbf{j} + (2 - 2z)\mathbf{k}$, $\boldsymbol{b} = 6\mathbf{i} + (5 - y)\,\mathbf{j} + (8 - 5z)$ and $2\boldsymbol{a} = -\boldsymbol{b}$.

2 Given that $\boldsymbol{a} = 3\mathbf{i} + 5\mathbf{j} + 3\mathbf{k}$, $\boldsymbol{b} = -3\mathbf{i} + 5\mathbf{j} + 2\mathbf{k}$, $\boldsymbol{c} = 4\mathbf{i} - 6\mathbf{j} - 3\mathbf{k}$, find
 (a) $3\boldsymbol{a} + 3\boldsymbol{b}$, (b) $4\boldsymbol{b} - 3\boldsymbol{a}$, (c) $2\boldsymbol{a} + 5\boldsymbol{b} + \boldsymbol{c}$, (d) $\boldsymbol{a} - 2\boldsymbol{b} + 3\boldsymbol{c}$.

3 Find the position vectors of the following points P(2, 3, 6), Q(4, −3, 8), R(−5, 4, −2), S(−2, 6, −7).

4 Find, for the points in the previous question, $\overrightarrow{PQ}$, $\overrightarrow{RS}$, $\overrightarrow{PS}$, $\overrightarrow{QR}$, $\overrightarrow{PR}$.

5 Find the magnitudes of the following vectors and the unit vectors along them.
 (a) $4\mathbf{i} - 2\mathbf{j} + 4\mathbf{k}$, (b) $5\mathbf{i} + 2\mathbf{j} + 6\mathbf{k}$, (c) $4\mathbf{i} + 6\mathbf{j} - 3\mathbf{k}$.

5.5 Scalar product of two dimensional vectors

Multiplication of vectors is rather complicated and there are two different products of two vectors. One product is the scalar product which is covered in your course, the other is the vector product which is not covered. The idea of the scalar product of two vectors is a very important one, particularly in Mechanics. Though the definition is the same for both two and three dimensional vectors, the algebra is slightly easier in two dimensions and it is therefore easier to look at this case first.

The scalar product of two vectors $\boldsymbol{a}$ and $\boldsymbol{b}$ is a scalar (i.e. a number) which is written as $\boldsymbol{a} \cdot \boldsymbol{b}$ and defined to be $ab \cos \theta$, where θ is the angle between $\boldsymbol{a}$ and $\boldsymbol{b}$. It is very important to always include the dot and underline the vectors, otherwise you could read it as ab which is not the same. In $\boldsymbol{a} \cdot \boldsymbol{a}$, i.e. the scalar product of $\boldsymbol{a}$ with itself, the angle θ is zero and, since $\cos 0 = 1$, $\boldsymbol{a} \cdot \boldsymbol{a} = a^2$. Therefore the magnitude of a vector is the square root of its scalar product with itself. Applying this to the unit vectors $\mathbf{i}$ and $\mathbf{j}$ gives

$$\mathbf{i} \cdot \mathbf{i} = 1, \quad \mathbf{j} \cdot \mathbf{j} = 1.$$

The angle between the unit vectors $\mathbf{i}$ and $\mathbf{j}$ is $90°$ and therefore, since $\cos 90° = 0$,

$$\mathbf{i} \cdot \mathbf{j} = 0 = \mathbf{j} \cdot \mathbf{i}.$$

Properties of the scalar product

(i) $\boldsymbol{a} \cdot \boldsymbol{b} = \boldsymbol{b} \cdot \boldsymbol{a}$, the definition is the same for both $\boldsymbol{a} \cdot \boldsymbol{b}$ and $\boldsymbol{b} \cdot \boldsymbol{a}$, so they are equal.

(ii) $\boldsymbol{a} \cdot (\boldsymbol{b} + \boldsymbol{c}) = \boldsymbol{a} \cdot \boldsymbol{b} + \boldsymbol{a} \cdot \boldsymbol{c}$ - the distributive law.

A proof of the distributive law in two dimensions is given in section 5.7.

The distributive law also implies that

$$(\boldsymbol{a} + \boldsymbol{d}) \cdot (\boldsymbol{b} + \boldsymbol{c}) = \boldsymbol{a} \cdot \boldsymbol{b} + \boldsymbol{a} \cdot \boldsymbol{c} + \boldsymbol{d} \cdot \boldsymbol{b} + \boldsymbol{d} \cdot \boldsymbol{c},$$

i.e. the scalar product of a sum of vectors is the sum of the separate scalar products.
This can be applied to the vectors $\boldsymbol{a} = a_x\,\mathbf{i} + a_y\,\mathbf{j}$ and $\boldsymbol{b} = b_x\,\mathbf{i} + b_y\,\mathbf{j}$ so that

$$\boldsymbol{a} \cdot \boldsymbol{b} = (a_x\,\mathbf{i} + a_y\,\mathbf{j}) \cdot (b_x\,\mathbf{i} + b_y\,\mathbf{j}) = a_x b_x\ \mathbf{i} \cdot \mathbf{i} + a_y\ b_y\ \mathbf{j} \cdot \mathbf{j} + a_y b_x\,\mathbf{j} \cdot \mathbf{i} + a_x b_y\ \mathbf{i} \cdot \mathbf{j}.$$

The above results for the scalar products of the unit vectors simplifies this result to

$$\boldsymbol{a} \cdot \boldsymbol{b} = a_x\,b_x + a_y\,b_y,$$

i.e the scalar product is the sum of the products of the corresponding components.
The expression for the scalar product in terms of components gives a quick way of finding the angle between two vectors, or lines.

Example 5.18

Find the angle between the vectors $4\mathbf{i} + 6\mathbf{j}$ and $7\mathbf{i} - 3\mathbf{j}$.

The scalar product of the vectors is $4 \times 7 - 6 \times 3 = 10$.

The magnitudes of the vectors are $\sqrt{4^2+6^2}$ and $\sqrt{7^2+3^2}$, therefore the definition of the scalar product shows that the scalar product of the two vectors is also $\sqrt{4^2+6^2} \times \sqrt{7^2+3^2} \times \cos\theta$ where θ is the angle between the vectors.
Therefore $\sqrt{4^2+6^2} \times \sqrt{7^2+3^2} \times \cos\theta = 10$ and $\theta = 79.5°$.

Using the method in the above example it is possible to get the following formula for the cosine of the angle between two vectors $\boldsymbol{a} = a_x\,\mathbf{i} + a_y\,\mathbf{j}$ and $\boldsymbol{b} = b_x\,\mathbf{i} + b_y\,\mathbf{j}$.

$$\cos\theta = \frac{a_x b_x + a_y b_y}{\sqrt{a_x^2 + a_y^2}\sqrt{b_x^2 + b_y^2}}.$$

It is not really worth trying to remember this formula as it is easier to carry out the calculations directly as in Example 5.18.

Distance between two points (i.e. | *b* – *a* |)

The scalar product can be used to find the distance between two points A and B, with position vectors $\boldsymbol{a}$ and $\boldsymbol{b}$ respectively. The vector $\overrightarrow{AB}$ is equal to $\boldsymbol{b} - \boldsymbol{a}$ and the distance between the points, i.e. the magnitude of $\overrightarrow{AB}$, is denoted by $|\,\boldsymbol{b} - \boldsymbol{a}\,|$. Also

$$AB^2 = \overrightarrow{AB}\,.\,\overrightarrow{AB} = (\boldsymbol{b} - \boldsymbol{a}).\,(\boldsymbol{b} - \boldsymbol{a}).$$

This can be expanded using the distributive law so that

$$AB^2 = |\boldsymbol{b} - \boldsymbol{a}\,|^2 = a^2 + b^2 - 2\boldsymbol{a}\,.\,\boldsymbol{b}.$$

This is actually the cosine rule as you can see by using $\boldsymbol{a}\,.\,\boldsymbol{b} = ab\cos\theta$.

Test for perpendicular vectors

The two vectors $\boldsymbol{a}$ and $\boldsymbol{b}$ will be perpendicular if $\cos\theta = 0$, i.e.

$$\boldsymbol{a}\,.\,\boldsymbol{b} = a_x b_x + a_y b_y = 0.$$

Construction of perpendicular vectors

The condition for two vectors to be perpendicular is satisfied if $b_y = a_x$ and $b_x = -\,a_y$. There are other possibilities but this gives the basic rule (**only for two dimensional vectors)** that a vector perpendicular to a given vector can be found by interchanging the components and changing the sign of one of them, e.g a vector perpendicular to $5\mathbf{i} + 11\mathbf{j}$ is $11\mathbf{i} - 5\mathbf{j}$.

Components (or resolute) of a vector

The component (or resolute) of a vector $\boldsymbol{a}$ in the direction of the unit vector $\boldsymbol{n}$ is, as stated earlier, defined to be $a\cos\theta$ where θ is the angle between $\boldsymbol{a}$ and $\boldsymbol{n}$. Since $\boldsymbol{n}$ is of unit magnitude, $a\cos\theta = \boldsymbol{a}\,.\,\boldsymbol{n}$. This gives a simple useful method of finding the component of a vector in a given direction, i.e. the component of $\boldsymbol{a}$ in the direction of the unit vector $\boldsymbol{n}$ is $\boldsymbol{a}\,.\,\boldsymbol{n}$.

Example 5.19

Find the resolute, in the direction of the vector 3**i** + 4**j**, of the vector 7**i** + 6**j**.

The first step is to find the unit vector in the required direction. The magnitude of 3**i** + 4**j** is 5 and the unit vector is therefore $\frac{3\mathbf{i}+4\mathbf{j}}{5}$. The required resolute is therefore

$$7 \times \frac{3}{5} + 6 \times \frac{4}{5} = 9.$$

Resolved part of a vector

The resolved part of a vector in a given direction is defined to be that part of the vector parallel to the given direction. For example, if $\boldsymbol{a} = a_x\,\mathbf{i} + a_y\,\mathbf{j}$ then $a_x\,\mathbf{i}$ is the resolved part of $\boldsymbol{a}$ in the direction **i**. The resolved part is therefore the resolute in a given direction multiplying the unit vector in that direction.

The resolved part of 7**i** + 6**j** in the direction of the vector 3**i** + 4**j** is, from Example 5.19,

$$9 \times \frac{3\mathbf{i}+4\mathbf{j}}{5} = \frac{27\mathbf{i}+36\mathbf{j}}{5}.$$

The remainder of 7**i** + 6**j** (i.e. the resolved part perpendicular to 3**i** + 4**j**) is therefore

$$7\mathbf{i} + 6\mathbf{j} - \frac{27\mathbf{i}+36\mathbf{j}}{5} = \frac{8\mathbf{i}-6\mathbf{j}}{5}.$$

For a general unit vector $\boldsymbol{n}$, the resolved part of $\boldsymbol{a}$ in the direction of the vector $\boldsymbol{n}$ is $(\boldsymbol{a}\,.\,\boldsymbol{n})\boldsymbol{n}$ and therefore the part of $\boldsymbol{a}$ perpendicular to $\boldsymbol{n}$ is $\boldsymbol{a} - (\boldsymbol{a}\,.\,\boldsymbol{n})\boldsymbol{n}$.

Exercises 5.4

1 Find the scalar products of the following pairs of vectors (a) 7**i** + 6**j** and 3**i** + 2**j**, (b) 2**i** – 6**j** and 5**i** – 6**j**, (c) –3**i** + 4**j** and **i** – 2**j**, (d) –2**i** – 5**j** and 4**i** – 3**j**.

2 Find the angles between the following pairs of vectors (a) 2**i** + 5**j** and **i** + 6**j**, (b) 3**i** – 5**j** and 4**i** – 7**j**, (c) – **i** + 5**j** and 2**i** – 5**j**, (d) –3**i** – 4**j** and 2**i** + 9**j**.

3 Obtain vectors perpendicular to (a) 4**i** + 7**j**, (b) 9**i** – 11**j**.

4 Find the angle between the line joining the points (1, 4) and (3, 2) and the line joining the points (5, 3) and (2, 8).

5 Find the angle between $\boldsymbol{a}$ and $\boldsymbol{b}$ in the following cases (a) $a = 2$, $b = 4$, $\boldsymbol{a}\,.\,\boldsymbol{b} = 3$, (b) $a = 4$, $b = 2$, $\boldsymbol{a}\,.\,\boldsymbol{b} = -4$.

6 Given that $a = 1$, $b = 6$, $\boldsymbol{a}\,.\,\boldsymbol{b} = 5$, find $|\,\boldsymbol{a} - \boldsymbol{b}\,|$ and $|\,\boldsymbol{a} + \boldsymbol{b}\,|$.

7 Find (a) the component of $\boldsymbol{a}$ in the direction of the vector $\boldsymbol{b}$, (b) the resolved part of $\boldsymbol{a}$ in the direction of the vector $\boldsymbol{b}$, (c) the resolved part of $\boldsymbol{a}$ in a direction perpendicular to the vector $\boldsymbol{b}$, for the cases (a) $\boldsymbol{a}$ = 11**i** + 4**j**, $\boldsymbol{b}$ = 3**i** – 4**j**, (b) $\boldsymbol{a}$ = 12**i** – 15**j**, $\boldsymbol{b}$ = 12**i** + 5 **j** .

5.6 Scalar product in three dimensions

The only difference between the scalar product in two dimensions and in three dimensions is that the vectors have three perpendicular components. The definition is exactly the same and the three unit vectors **i**, **j**, and **k** have now to satisfy

$$\mathbf{i}\,.\,\mathbf{i} = 1,\ \ \mathbf{j}\,.\,\mathbf{j} = 1,\ \ \mathbf{k}\,.\,\mathbf{k} = 1,$$

$$\mathbf{i}\,.\,\mathbf{j} = 0 = \mathbf{j}\,.\,\mathbf{i},\ \ \mathbf{i}\,.\,\mathbf{k} = 0 = \mathbf{k}\,.\,\mathbf{i},\ \ \mathbf{j}\,.\,\mathbf{k} = 0 = \mathbf{k}\,.\,\mathbf{j}.$$

The distributive law is still satisfied and applying it to $\boldsymbol{a} = a_x\,\mathbf{i} + a_y\,\mathbf{j} + a_z\,\mathbf{k}$ and $\boldsymbol{b} = b_x\,\mathbf{i} + b_y\,\mathbf{j} + b_z\,\mathbf{k}$, and using the equations satisfied by **i**, **j**, and **k** gives

$$\boldsymbol{a}\,.\,\boldsymbol{b} = a_x\,b_x + a_y\,b_y + a_z\,b_z\,.$$

The expression for the scalar product is slightly longer but is still the sum of the products of the corresponding components.

Angle between a vector and the axes

If θ is the angle between the vector 3**i** + 4**j** + 12**k** and the unit vector **i** then, since the unit vector has unit magnitude, **i**.(3**i** + 4**j** + 12**k**) = $\sqrt{3^2 + 4^2 + 12^2}$ cos θ so that cos θ = $\frac{3}{13}$ and θ = 76.7°. The cosine is therefore the ratio of the corresponding component to the magnitude of the vector and you would find a similar result if you tried to find the angles between the vector and the other two unit vectors.

The general result is that the cosines of the angles between the vector $\boldsymbol{a} = a_x\,\mathbf{i} + a_y\,\mathbf{j} + a_z\,\mathbf{k}$ and the unit vectors **i**, **j**, and **k** are, respectively,

$$\frac{a_x}{\sqrt{a_x^2 + a_y^2 + a_z^2}},\quad \frac{a_y}{\sqrt{a_x^2 + a_y^2 + a_z^2}},\quad \frac{a_z}{\sqrt{a_x^2 + a_y^2 + a_z^2}}.$$

The only idea in two dimensions which does not carry over into three dimensions is the construction of perpendicular vectors. The condition to be satisfied is

$$a_x\,b_x + a_y\,b_y + a_z\,b_z = 0,$$

but it is not possible to give a simple solution for this.

Example 5.20

Find the angle between the vectors 2**i** + 4**j** + 3**k** and 3**i** – 2**j** + **k**.

The scalar product of the vectors is 2 × 3 + 4 × (–2) + 3 × 1 = 1.
The magnitudes of the vectors are $\sqrt{2^2 + 4^2 + 3^2} = \sqrt{29}$ and $\sqrt{3^2 + 2^2 + 1^2} = \sqrt{14}$.
Therefore, if θ is the angle between the vectors, $\sqrt{29} \times \sqrt{14} \times \cos\theta = 1$ so that θ = 87.2°.

Example 5.21

Find

(a) the component of $4\mathbf{i} + 7\mathbf{j} - 2\mathbf{k}$ in the direction of the vector $2\mathbf{i} - \mathbf{j} + 2\mathbf{k}$,

(b) the resolved part of $4\mathbf{i} + 7\mathbf{j} - 2\mathbf{k}$ in the direction of the vector $2\mathbf{i} - \mathbf{j} + 2\mathbf{k}$,

(c) the resolved part of $4\mathbf{i} + 7\mathbf{j} - 2\mathbf{k}$ perpendicular to the vector $2\mathbf{i} - \mathbf{j} + 2\mathbf{k}$.

(a) The magnitude of $2\mathbf{i} - \mathbf{j} + 2\mathbf{k}$ is $\sqrt{2^2 + 1^2 + 2^2} = 3$, the unit vector in the direction of the vector $2\mathbf{i} - \mathbf{j} + 2\mathbf{k}$ is therefore $\dfrac{-2\mathbf{i} + \mathbf{j} - 2\mathbf{k}}{3}$ and the required component or resolute is $4 \times \dfrac{2}{3} + 7 \times \dfrac{-1}{3} - 2 \times \dfrac{2}{3} = -1$.

(b) The resolved part is the product of the unit vector and the component in its direction i.e. $\dfrac{-2\mathbf{i} + \mathbf{j} - 2\mathbf{k}}{3}$.

(c) The resolved part perpendicular to $2\mathbf{i} - \mathbf{j} + 2\mathbf{k}$ is found by subtracting the result of (b) from $4\mathbf{i} + 7\mathbf{j} - 2\mathbf{k}$, this gives $\dfrac{14\mathbf{i} + 20\mathbf{j} - 4\mathbf{k}}{3}$.

You can check that the scalar product of this with $2\mathbf{i} - \mathbf{j} + 2\mathbf{k}$ vanishes so that the vectors are perpendicular.

5.7 Proof of distributive law for scalar product

The vectors $\boldsymbol{a}$, $\boldsymbol{b}$, and $\boldsymbol{c}$, are assumed to be coplanar and, in the diagram,

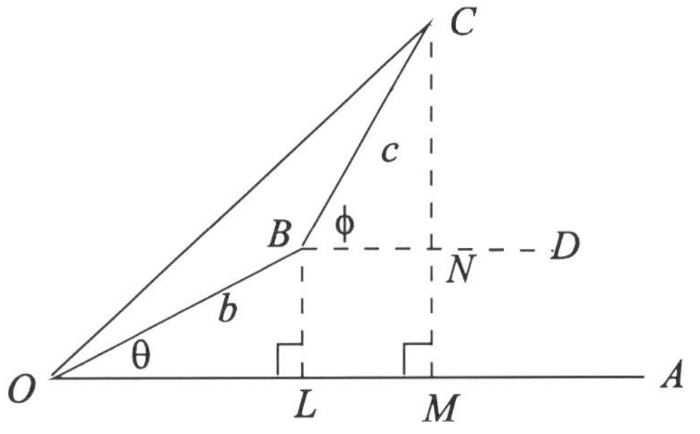

$\overrightarrow{OA} = \boldsymbol{a}$, $\overrightarrow{OB} = \boldsymbol{b}$, $\overrightarrow{BC} = \boldsymbol{c}$, and therefore $\boldsymbol{b} + \boldsymbol{c} = \overrightarrow{OC}$. Perpendiculars BL and CM are drawn from B and C to OA, the line BD is drawn through B parallel to $\boldsymbol{a}$ and CN is the perpendicular from C to BD. The angles between OA and OB and between BD and BC are denoted by θ and ϕ, respectively.

$$\boldsymbol{a}.\boldsymbol{b} = ab \cos\theta = a\,OL, \quad \boldsymbol{a}.\boldsymbol{c} = ac\cos\phi = a\,BN = a\,LM,$$

$$\boldsymbol{a}.(\boldsymbol{b} + \boldsymbol{c}) = a\,OC \cos C\hat{O}M = a\,OM.$$

Since $OM = OL + LM$ this gives

$$\boldsymbol{a}.\boldsymbol{b} + \boldsymbol{a}.\boldsymbol{c} = a\,OL + a\,LM = a\,OM = \boldsymbol{a}.(\boldsymbol{b} + \boldsymbol{c}).$$

The proof for three dimensional vectors requires some use of ideas from three dimensional geometry and will not be given.

Exercises 5.5

1 Find the scalar products of the following pairs of vectors

(a) $2\mathbf{i} + 4\mathbf{j} - 3\mathbf{k}$ and $\mathbf{i} + 6\mathbf{j} - 4\mathbf{k}$, (b) $3\mathbf{i} - \mathbf{j} + 6\mathbf{k}$ and $\mathbf{i} - 2\mathbf{j} - 3\mathbf{k}$,

(c) $8\mathbf{i} + 5\mathbf{j} - 3\mathbf{k}$ and $\mathbf{i} + \mathbf{j} - \mathbf{k}$, (d) $3\mathbf{i} - 2\mathbf{j} + 5\mathbf{k}$ and $2\mathbf{i} + \mathbf{j} - 2\mathbf{k}$.

2 Determine which of the following pairs of vectors are perpendicular to each other and find the angles between those pairs that are not perpendicular to each other,

(a) $2\mathbf{i} + 4\mathbf{j} - 2\mathbf{k}$ and $\mathbf{i} + 6\mathbf{j} + 13\mathbf{k}$, (b) $2\mathbf{i} - 4\mathbf{j} + 3\mathbf{k}$ and $\mathbf{i} - 3\mathbf{j} - 2\mathbf{k}$,

(c) $4\mathbf{i} + 7\mathbf{j} - 3\mathbf{k}$ and $\mathbf{i} + 2\mathbf{j} - \mathbf{k}$, (d) $3\mathbf{i} - 4\mathbf{j} + 5\mathbf{k}$ and $\mathbf{i} + 2\mathbf{j} + \mathbf{k}$.

3 Find the angle between the line joining the points (1, 4, 6) and (3, 2, 1) and the line joining the points (5, 3, 5) and (2, 8, 4).

4 Given that $\boldsymbol{a}^2 = 6$, $\boldsymbol{b}^2 = 2$, $\boldsymbol{a}.\boldsymbol{b} = 2$, find $|\,2\boldsymbol{a} + 3\boldsymbol{b}\,|$, $|\,3\boldsymbol{a} - 2\boldsymbol{b}\,|$.

5 Given that $\boldsymbol{a} = 5\mathbf{i} - 3\mathbf{j} - 4\mathbf{k}$, and $\boldsymbol{b} = \mathbf{i} + 2\mathbf{j} - 2\mathbf{k}$, find the scalar p such that $p\boldsymbol{a} + \boldsymbol{b}$ is perpendicular to $\boldsymbol{a}$.

6 Given that $\boldsymbol{a} = 5\mathbf{i} + \mathbf{j} - 3\mathbf{k}$, and $\boldsymbol{b} = \mathbf{i} + 3\mathbf{j} - 5\mathbf{k}$, show that the vectors $\boldsymbol{a} + \boldsymbol{b}$ and $\boldsymbol{a} - \boldsymbol{b}$ are perpendicular to each other.

7 Find (a) the resolute of $\boldsymbol{a}$ in the direction of the vector $\boldsymbol{b}$, (b) the resolved part of $\boldsymbol{a}$ in the direction of the vector $\boldsymbol{b}$, (c) the resolved part of $\boldsymbol{a}$ in a direction perpendicular to the vector $\boldsymbol{b}$, for the cases

(a) $\boldsymbol{a} = 5\mathbf{i} + 6\mathbf{j} + 3\mathbf{k}$, $\boldsymbol{b} = 2\mathbf{i} + \mathbf{j} + 2\mathbf{k}$,

(b) $\boldsymbol{a} = 3\mathbf{i} + 7\mathbf{j} - 2\mathbf{k}$, $\boldsymbol{b} = 3\mathbf{i} + 4\mathbf{j} + 12\mathbf{k}$.

5.8 Differentiation and integration of vectors

The components of a vector, and therefore the vector, can vary with time.
For example in the diagram the point P is describing a circle about the point O.

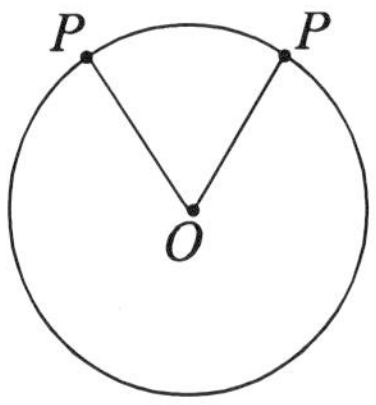

Although the length OP stays the same, the direction of $\overrightarrow{OP}$ varies and therefore the vector $\overrightarrow{OP}$ varies with time. The derivative of a vector with respect to time effectively measures the rate of change of the vector with respect to time and is itself a vector. It is possible to define the derivative of a vector as a limit, roughly as in your P1 course, but this is rather more general than is needed in Mechanics where it is

sufficient to give a simple definition of the derivative in component form, where the unit vectors are assumed not to vary with time. A vector can change with respect to any parameter and the basic definition is the same whatever the parameter.
The idea of differentiating and integrating vectors is very important in kinematics and dynamics and the basic definitions given in this section will be used in sections 7.2 and 7.3.

Differentiation

In this definition it is assumed that the unit vectors **i**, **j** and **k** do not depend on *t*.

The derivative $\frac{\mathrm{d}\boldsymbol{a}}{\mathrm{d}t}$ of a vector $\boldsymbol{a}$ with respect to t is the vector whose components are the derivatives with respect to t of the components of $\boldsymbol{a}$, i.e. if $\boldsymbol{a} = a_x\,\mathbf{i} + a_y\,\mathbf{j} + a_z\,\mathbf{j}$ then

$$\frac{\mathrm{d}\boldsymbol{a}}{\mathrm{d}t} = \frac{\mathrm{d}a_x}{\mathrm{d}t}\,\mathbf{i} + \frac{\mathrm{d}a_y}{\mathrm{d}t}\,\mathbf{j} + \frac{\mathrm{d}\,a_z}{\mathrm{d}t}\,\mathbf{k}.$$

If a vector is constant then all its components are constant, their derivatives are therefore zero and therefore the derivative of a constant vector is the zero vector.

Integration

In this definition it is assumed that the unit vectors **i**, **j** and **k** do not depend on *t*.
The integral $\int \boldsymbol{a}\,\mathrm{d}t$ of a vector $\boldsymbol{a}$ is the vector whose components are the integrals of the components of $\boldsymbol{a}$, i.e. if $\boldsymbol{a} = a_x\,\mathbf{i} + a_y\,\mathbf{j} + a_z\,\mathbf{j}$ then

$$\int \boldsymbol{a}\,\mathrm{d}t = \int a_x\,\mathrm{d}t\;\mathbf{i} + \int a_y\,\mathrm{d}t\;\mathbf{j} + \int a_z\,\mathrm{d}t\;\mathbf{k}.$$

When a vector is integrated, a constant vector of integration has to be introduced where, for scalars, a constant of integration is introduced.

Rules for differentiation and integration

(i) $\frac{\mathrm{d}(\boldsymbol{a}+\boldsymbol{b})}{\mathrm{d}t} = \frac{\mathrm{d}\boldsymbol{a}}{\mathrm{d}t} + \frac{\mathrm{d}\boldsymbol{b}}{\mathrm{d}t}$.

(ii) $\frac{\mathrm{d}(m\boldsymbol{a})}{\mathrm{d}t} = m\frac{\mathrm{d}\boldsymbol{a}}{\mathrm{d}t} + \boldsymbol{a}\frac{\mathrm{d}m}{\mathrm{d}t}$.

(iii) For $\boldsymbol{a}$ constant $\frac{\mathrm{d}(m\boldsymbol{a})}{\mathrm{d}t} = \boldsymbol{a}\frac{\mathrm{d}m}{\mathrm{d}t}$, i.e. the derivative of a scalar multiplying a constant vector is the product of the constant vector and the derivative of the scalar.

(iv) $\frac{\mathrm{d}(\boldsymbol{a}.\boldsymbol{b})}{\mathrm{d}t} = \boldsymbol{a}\,.\frac{\mathrm{d}\boldsymbol{b}}{\mathrm{d}t} + \boldsymbol{b}\,.\frac{\mathrm{d}\boldsymbol{a}}{\mathrm{d}t}$.

(v) For $\boldsymbol{a} = \boldsymbol{b}$ rule (iv) becomes $\frac{\mathrm{d}(\boldsymbol{a}.\boldsymbol{a})}{\mathrm{d}t} = 2\boldsymbol{a}.\frac{\mathrm{d}\boldsymbol{a}}{\mathrm{d}t}$.

Also $\boldsymbol{a}.\,\boldsymbol{a} = a^2$ and therefore $\frac{\mathrm{d}(a^2)}{\mathrm{d}t} = 2\boldsymbol{a}.\frac{\mathrm{d}\boldsymbol{a}}{\mathrm{d}t}$.

From this last result it follows that for any vector $\boldsymbol{a}$ of constant magnitude, and therefore any unit vector, $\boldsymbol{a}$ is perpendicular to $\frac{\mathrm{d}\boldsymbol{a}}{\mathrm{d}t}$ since $\frac{\mathrm{d}(a^2)}{\mathrm{d}t}$ is then zero.

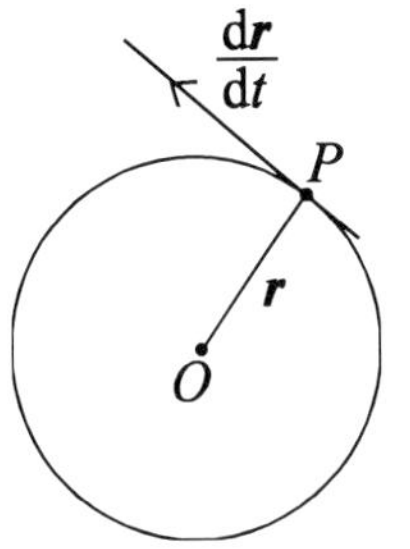

This means that when, as in the diagram, a point P, with position vector $\boldsymbol{r}$ relative to O, describes a circle centre O, $\frac{\mathrm{d}\boldsymbol{r}}{\mathrm{d}t}$ will be perpendicular to the radius i.e. along the tangent, though its sense may be opposite to that shown.

(vi) $\int(\boldsymbol{a}+\boldsymbol{b})\mathrm{d}t = \int\boldsymbol{a}\mathrm{d}t + \int\boldsymbol{b}\mathrm{d}t$.

(vii) If $\boldsymbol{a}$ is a constant vector then $\int m\boldsymbol{a}\mathrm{d}t = \boldsymbol{a}\int m\mathrm{d}t$, i.e. the integral of the product of a scalar and a constant vector is the integral of the scalar multiplied by the constant vector.

You can check all of these by applying the definition of the derivative and integral to both sides of the equations.

Example 5.22

Find $\frac{\mathrm{d}\boldsymbol{a}}{\mathrm{d}t}$ and $\frac{\mathrm{d}^2\boldsymbol{a}}{\mathrm{d}t^2}$ for (a) $\boldsymbol{a} = t^2\,\mathbf{i} + 4\cos t\,\mathbf{j}$, (b) $\boldsymbol{a} = \mathrm{e}^{-t}\,\mathbf{i} + t^3\,\mathbf{j} + 4t^2\,\mathbf{k}$.

(a) $$\frac{\mathrm{d}\boldsymbol{a}}{\mathrm{d}t} = \frac{\mathrm{d}t^2}{\mathrm{d}t}\,\mathbf{i} + 4\frac{\mathrm{d}\cos t}{\mathrm{d}t}\,\mathbf{j} = 2t\,\mathbf{i} - 4\sin t\,\mathbf{j},$$

$$\frac{\mathrm{d}^2\boldsymbol{a}}{\mathrm{d}t^2} = \frac{\mathrm{d}\frac{\mathrm{d}\boldsymbol{a}}{\mathrm{d}t}}{\mathrm{d}t} = 2\frac{\mathrm{d}t}{\mathrm{d}t}\,\mathbf{i} - 4\frac{\mathrm{d}\sin t}{\mathrm{d}t}\,\mathbf{j} = 2\mathbf{i} - 4\cos t\,\mathbf{j}.$$

(b) $$\frac{\mathrm{d}\boldsymbol{a}}{\mathrm{d}t} = \frac{\mathrm{d}\mathrm{e}^{-t}}{\mathrm{d}t}\,\mathbf{i} + \frac{\mathrm{d}t^3}{\mathrm{d}t}\,\mathbf{j} + 4\frac{\mathrm{d}t^2}{\mathrm{d}t}\,\mathbf{k} = -\mathrm{e}^{-t}\,\mathbf{i} + 3t^2\,\mathbf{j} + 8t\,\mathbf{k},$$

$$\frac{\mathrm{d}^2\boldsymbol{a}}{\mathrm{d}t^2} = \frac{\mathrm{d}\frac{\mathrm{d}\boldsymbol{a}}{\mathrm{d}t}}{\mathrm{d}t} = -\frac{\mathrm{d}\mathrm{e}^{-t}}{\mathrm{d}t}\,\mathbf{i} + 3\frac{\mathrm{d}t^2}{\mathrm{d}t}\,\mathbf{j} + 8\frac{\mathrm{d}t}{\mathrm{d}t}\,\mathbf{k} = \mathrm{e}^{-t}\,\mathbf{i} + 6t\,\mathbf{j} + 8\mathbf{k}.$$

Example 5.23

Given that $\boldsymbol{a}$ is a constant vector find the derivatives with respect to t of
(a) $t^2\,\boldsymbol{a}$, (b) $t^2\,\boldsymbol{a} + \cos t\mathbf{a}$.

(a) The components of $\boldsymbol{a}$ are not given and therefore rule (iii) above gives

$$\frac{\mathrm{d}t^2\mathbf{a}}{\mathrm{d}t} = \frac{\mathrm{d}t^2}{\mathrm{d}t}\,\boldsymbol{a} = 2t\boldsymbol{a}.$$

(b) In this case rule (i) for differentiating a sum of vectors has to be used first and then followed by applying rule (iii) for differentiating the product of a scalar and a vector. This gives

$$\frac{\mathrm{d}(t^3\mathrm{a} + \cos t\mathbf{a})}{\mathrm{d}t} = \frac{\mathrm{d}(t^3\mathbf{a})}{\mathrm{d}t} + \frac{\mathrm{d}(\cos t\,\mathbf{a})}{\mathrm{d}t}$$

$$= \frac{\mathrm{d}t^3}{\mathrm{d}t}\,\boldsymbol{a} + \frac{\mathrm{d}\cos t}{\mathrm{d}t}\,\boldsymbol{a} = 3t^2\,\boldsymbol{a} - \sin t\boldsymbol{a}.$$

Example 5.24

Find the integrals with respect to time of the vectors
(a) $2t\,\mathbf{i} + 4\sin t\,\mathbf{j}$, (b) $2\,\mathrm{e}^{-2t}\mathbf{i} + \mathbf{j} + 3t^2\;\mathbf{k}$.

(a) The integral is found by integrating the components and including a constant vector of integration. This gives $t^2\;\mathbf{i} - 4\cos t\,\mathbf{j} + \boldsymbol{b}$, where $\boldsymbol{b}$ is a constant vector.
(b) Integrating the components in this case gives $-\,\mathrm{e}^{-2t}\mathbf{i} + t\,\mathbf{j} + t^3\;\mathbf{k} + \boldsymbol{b}$, where $\boldsymbol{b}$ is a constant vector.

Example 5.25

Given that $\boldsymbol{a}$ is a constant vector, find the integral with respect to t of
(a) $\boldsymbol{a}$, (b) $3t^2\;\boldsymbol{a}$.

(a) Rule (vii) above gives the integral as $t\,\mathbf{a} + \boldsymbol{b}$, where $\boldsymbol{b}$ is a constant vector.
(b) Rule (vi) above gives the integral as $t^3\;\mathbf{a} + \boldsymbol{b}$, where $\boldsymbol{b}$ is a constant vector.

Example 5.26

Given that $\frac{\mathrm{d}\boldsymbol{r}}{\mathrm{d}t} = 2t\,\mathbf{i} + \sin t\,\mathbf{j} + \mathrm{e}^{-t}\,\mathbf{k}$, and that $\boldsymbol{r} = 2\mathbf{i} + 3\mathbf{j} + 4\mathbf{k}$, when $t = 0$, find $\boldsymbol{r}$.

The first step is integrating $\frac{\mathrm{d}\boldsymbol{r}}{\mathrm{d}t}$ to find $\boldsymbol{r}$ for time t. This gives $\boldsymbol{r} = t^2\;\mathbf{i} - \cos t\,\mathbf{j} - \mathrm{e}^{-t}\,\mathbf{k} + \boldsymbol{b}$, where $\boldsymbol{b}$ is a constant vector. Substituting the value of $\boldsymbol{r}$ given for $t = 0$ shows that

$$2\mathbf{i} + 3\mathbf{j} + 4\mathbf{k} = -\,\mathbf{j} - \mathbf{k} + \boldsymbol{b}.$$

Solving this gives $\boldsymbol{b} = 2\mathbf{i} + 4\mathbf{j} + 5\mathbf{k}$ and so

$$\boldsymbol{r} = t^2\;\mathbf{i} - \cos t\,\mathbf{j} - \mathrm{e}^{t}\,\mathbf{k} + 2\mathbf{i} + 4\mathbf{j} + 5\mathbf{k}.$$

Exercises 5.6

1 Find $\dfrac{d\boldsymbol{a}}{dt}$ and $\dfrac{d^2\boldsymbol{a}}{dt^2}$ for (a) $\boldsymbol{a} = 2t\,\mathbf{i} + 5t^4\,\mathbf{j}$, (b) $\boldsymbol{a} = e^t\,\mathbf{i} + t^3\mathbf{j}$,

(c) $\boldsymbol{a} = \cos t\,\mathbf{i} + \sin 2t\,\mathbf{j}$, (d) $\boldsymbol{a} = t^2\,\mathbf{i} + t\,\mathbf{j} + t^3\,\mathbf{k}$, (e) $\boldsymbol{a} = \cos t\,\mathbf{i} + t^4\,\mathbf{j} + \sin 3t\,\mathbf{k}$,

(f) $\boldsymbol{a} = e^{2t}\,\mathbf{i} + \cos t\,\mathbf{j} + \ln t\,\mathbf{k}$.

2 Given that $\boldsymbol{a}$ and $\boldsymbol{b}$ are constant vectors find the derivative with respect to t of

(a) $\dfrac{\boldsymbol{a}}{t}$, (b) $\boldsymbol{a}\cos t + t^2\,\boldsymbol{b}$, (c) $e^t\,\boldsymbol{a} + 2\,e^{-t}\,\boldsymbol{b}$.

3 Given that $\boldsymbol{r} = \cos nt\,\boldsymbol{a} + \sin nt\,\boldsymbol{b}$, where $\boldsymbol{a}$ and $\boldsymbol{b}$ are constant vectors and n is a constant, find the relationship between $\boldsymbol{r}$ and $\dfrac{d^2\boldsymbol{r}}{dt^2}$.

4 Integrate the following expressions with respect to t, (a) $4t^3\,\mathbf{i} + 6t^5\,\mathbf{j}$,

(b) $2e^{2t}\,\mathbf{i} + t^2\,\mathbf{j}$, (c) $2\cos 2t\,\mathbf{i} + \sin t\,\mathbf{j}$, (d) $3t^2\,\mathbf{i} + 2t\,\mathbf{j} + 4t^3\,\mathbf{k}$,

(e) $2\cos t\,\mathbf{i} + 5t^4\,\mathbf{j} + 4\sin t\,\mathbf{k}$, (f) $2e^{2t}\,\mathbf{i} + 4\cos 4t\,\mathbf{j} + 2t\,\mathbf{k}$.

5 Evaluate (a) $\displaystyle\int_{-1}^{2}(12t^3\mathbf{i} + 15t^4\mathbf{j})\,dt$, (b) $\displaystyle\int_{-1}^{2}(6t^5\mathbf{i} + 4t\mathbf{j} + 8t^3\mathbf{k})\,dt$.

6 Find $\boldsymbol{r}$ when (a) $\dfrac{d\boldsymbol{r}}{dt} = 7t^6\,\mathbf{i} + 3t^2\,\mathbf{j}$ and $\boldsymbol{r} = 4\mathbf{i} + 6\,\mathbf{j}$ for $t = 1$,

(b) $\dfrac{d\boldsymbol{r}}{dt} = 3t^2\,\mathbf{i} + 2t\,\mathbf{j} + 4t^3\mathbf{k}$ and $\boldsymbol{r} = 6\mathbf{i} + 7\mathbf{j} + 8\mathbf{k}$ for $t = 1$.

7 Find an expression for $\boldsymbol{r}$ when $\dfrac{d^2\boldsymbol{r}}{dt^2} = \boldsymbol{a}$, where $\boldsymbol{a}$ is a constant vector.

Miscellaneous Exercises 5

1

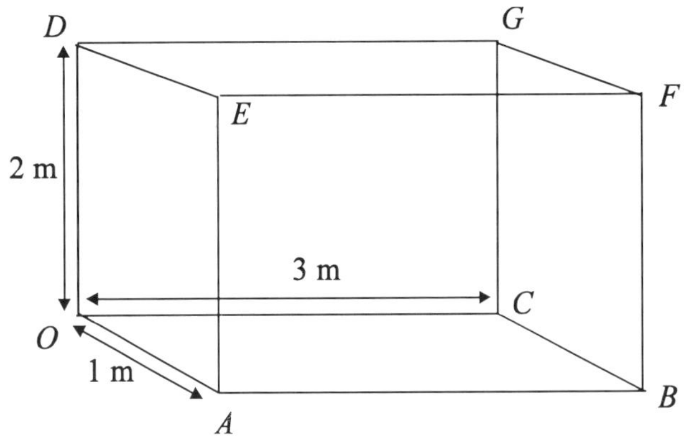

The figure shows a cuboid in which $OA = 1$ m, $OC = 3$ m and $OD = 2$ m. Taking O as origin and the unit vectors $\mathbf{i}$, $\mathbf{j}$ and $\mathbf{k}$ in the directions OA, OC and OD, respectively, express in terms of $\mathbf{i}$, $\mathbf{j}$ and $\mathbf{k}$ the vectors (a) $\overrightarrow{OF}$ and (b) $\overrightarrow{AG}$. By considering an appropriate scalar product, find the acute angle between the diagonals OF and AG.

2 The vectors $\boldsymbol{a}$, $\boldsymbol{b}$ and $\boldsymbol{c}$ are given by

$$\boldsymbol{a} = \mathbf{i} + 2\mathbf{j} + \mathbf{k},\ \boldsymbol{b} = \mathbf{i} + \mathbf{j} + 2\mathbf{k},\ \boldsymbol{c} = \mathbf{j} + \mathbf{k}.$$

A fourth vector is given by $\boldsymbol{d} = 3\mathbf{i} + 6\mathbf{j} + 5\mathbf{k}$.

Find the values of α, β and γ so that $\boldsymbol{d} = \alpha\boldsymbol{a} + \beta\boldsymbol{b} + \gamma\boldsymbol{c}$.

3 The coordinates of three points P, Q and R are $(9, 2, -4)$, $(3, 1, -4)$ and $(2, 7, 6)$ respectively. Find the vectors $\overrightarrow{PQ}$ and $\overrightarrow{QR}$ and show that they are perpendicular to each other.

4 Vectors $\boldsymbol{p}$, $\boldsymbol{q}$ and $\boldsymbol{r}$ are such that $|\boldsymbol{p} + \boldsymbol{q}| = |\boldsymbol{p} - 3\boldsymbol{q}| = |2\boldsymbol{p} - \boldsymbol{q}|$.

Find the ratio $\frac{p}{q}$ and the angle between the vectors $\boldsymbol{p}$ and $\boldsymbol{q}$.

5 The vectors $\overrightarrow{OA}$, $\overrightarrow{OB}$ and $\overrightarrow{OC}$ are given by

$$\overrightarrow{OA} = -2\mathbf{i} + 3\mathbf{j} - 7\mathbf{k},$$
$$\overrightarrow{OB} = \mathbf{i} + 7\mathbf{j} + 5\mathbf{k},$$
$$\overrightarrow{OC} = 4\mathbf{i} + 3\mathbf{j} + \mathbf{k}.$$

Show that $\overrightarrow{AB} = 3\mathbf{i} + 4\mathbf{j} + 12\mathbf{k}$ and obtain a similar expression for $\overrightarrow{AC}$.

Calculate $|\overrightarrow{AB}|$ and $|\overrightarrow{AC}|$ and the scalar product $\overrightarrow{AB} \cdot \overrightarrow{AC}$ and show that $\cos B\hat{A}C = \frac{57}{65}$.

6 The points A, B, C and D have position vectors $\mathbf{i} - 2\mathbf{j} + 5\mathbf{k}$, $\mathbf{i} + 3\mathbf{j}$, $10\mathbf{i} + \mathbf{j} + 2\mathbf{k}$, $-2\mathbf{i} + 4\mathbf{j} + 5\mathbf{k}$ respectively. The points P and Q lie on AB and CD, respectively, and $AP = \lambda AB$, $CQ = \mu CD$, where λ and μ are constants. Show that

$$\overrightarrow{OP} = \mathbf{i} + (5\lambda - 2)\mathbf{j} + 5(1 - \lambda)\mathbf{k},$$

and find a similar expression for $\overrightarrow{OQ}$.

Given that PQ is perpendicular to both AB and CD, obtain a pair of simultaneous equations for λ and μ. By solving these show that

$$\overrightarrow{PQ} = \mathbf{i} + 2\mathbf{j} + 2\mathbf{k}.$$

7 The vectors $\boldsymbol{a}$, $\boldsymbol{b}$ and $\boldsymbol{c}$ are defined by $\boldsymbol{a} = \mathbf{i} - 2\mathbf{j} + \mathbf{k}$, $\boldsymbol{b} = 2\mathbf{i} + \mathbf{j} - \mathbf{k}$, $\boldsymbol{c} = p\boldsymbol{a} + q\boldsymbol{b}$, where p and q are constants.

Given that $\boldsymbol{c}$ is perpendicular to $\boldsymbol{a}$, find $\frac{p}{q}$.

8 Find the resolved parts of the vector $2\mathbf{i} - \mathbf{j} + 3\mathbf{k}$ along and perpendicular to the vector $3\mathbf{i} + 2\mathbf{j} - 2\mathbf{k}$.

9 Given the vectors $\boldsymbol{a} = 3\mathbf{i} + 2\mathbf{j}$, $\boldsymbol{b} = 2\mathbf{i} + m\mathbf{j}$, find the values of m so that

(a) $\boldsymbol{a}$ and $\boldsymbol{b}$ are perpendicular to each other,

(b) $\boldsymbol{a}$ and $\boldsymbol{b}$ are parallel,

(c) the acute angle between $\boldsymbol{a}$ and $\boldsymbol{b}$ is $\frac{\pi}{4}$.

10 The position vectors of A and B with respect to a fixed origin are $\mathbf{i} + 2\mathbf{j} + \mathbf{k}$ and $5\mathbf{i} - 2\mathbf{j} + 3\mathbf{k}$. Find AB and the cosines of the angles between $\overrightarrow{AB}$ and the coordinate axes.

11 Find a unit vector perpendicular to both $4\mathbf{i} + 4\mathbf{j} - 7\mathbf{k}$ and $2\mathbf{i} + 2\mathbf{j} + \mathbf{k}$.

12 The position vectors of the four points A, B, C and D are $\mathbf{j} + 2\mathbf{k}$, $-\mathbf{i} - \mathbf{j}$, $4\mathbf{i} + \mathbf{k}$ and $3\mathbf{i} + \mathbf{j} + 2\mathbf{k}$ respectively. Show that the triangle ABC is right-angled and that the triangle ABD is isosceles.

Chapter 6

Applications of vectors

After working through this chapter you should

- be able to find, in component form, the resultant of forces acting at a point,
- be able to find the work done by constant forces in two and three dimensions,
- be able to determine the velocity and acceleration of a particle in two and three dimensions,
- be able to solve intercept and shortest distance of approach problems,
- understand the concepts of impulse, momentum, power, kinetic energy for general motions and be able to calculate these quantities in particular cases,
- be able to calculate the work done in a given time by a force whose components are given in terms of time.

6.1 Statics

You have already met the use of vectors in Statics, though in a slightly disguised form.

Resultant of forces acting at a point

The resultant of several forces acting at a point is the vector sum of the individual forces i.e. the components of the resultant are the sum of the corresponding components of the individual forces. This is exactly the definition you used in Chapter 2 of M1. The main difference now is that use of the unit vectors **i**, **j** and **k** makes the problems easier to state and the calculations appear simpler.

Example 6.1

Find the resultant of

(a) the forces $(4\mathbf{i} + 3\mathbf{j})$ N, $(5\,\mathbf{i} - 5\mathbf{j})$ N, $(2\mathbf{i} + 7\mathbf{j})$ N, acting at a point,

(b) the forces $(2\mathbf{i} + 4\mathbf{j} + 6\mathbf{k})$ N, $(9\mathbf{i} - 3\mathbf{j} + 4\mathbf{k})$ N, $(7\mathbf{i} + 2\mathbf{j} + 11\mathbf{k})$ N, acting at a point.

(a) The resultant is just the vector sum i.e.

$$(4\mathbf{i} + 3\mathbf{j} + 5\mathbf{i} - 5\mathbf{j} + 2\mathbf{i} + 7\mathbf{j})\text{ N} = (11\mathbf{i} + 5\mathbf{j})\text{ N}.$$

(b) Again the resultant is just the vector sum i.e.

$$(2\mathbf{i} + 4\mathbf{j} + 6\mathbf{k} + 9\mathbf{i} - 3\mathbf{j} + 4\mathbf{k} + 7\mathbf{i} + 2\mathbf{j} + 11\mathbf{k})\text{ N} = (18\mathbf{i} + 3\mathbf{j} + 21\mathbf{k})\text{ N}.$$

Example 6.2

Find the possible values of p such that the resultant of the three forces $(2\mathbf{i} + 5\mathbf{j} + 3\mathbf{k})$ N, $(p\mathbf{i} - 2\mathbf{j} + 7\mathbf{k})$ N, $(3\mathbf{i} + 7\mathbf{j} + 5\mathbf{k})$ N acting at a point has magnitude $\sqrt{389}$ N.

The resultant is

$(2\mathbf{i} + 5\mathbf{j} + 3\mathbf{k} + p\mathbf{i} - 2\mathbf{j} + 7\mathbf{k} + 3\mathbf{i} + 7\mathbf{j} + 5\mathbf{k})$ N $= ((p + 5)\mathbf{i} + 10\mathbf{j} + 15\mathbf{k})$ N.

Therefore, squaring and adding the components gives,

$$(p + 5)^2 + 10^2 + 15^2 = 389.$$

This gives $p + 5 = \pm 8$ and therefore $p = -13$ or 3.

Equilibrium of coplanar forces acting at a point

A system of forces acting at a point is in equilibrium if the vector sum is zero i.e. the components of the resultant in three perpendicular directions are zero. The only equilibrium problems you will come across in your course will involve coplanar forces. In this case the components of the resultant in two different directions are zero and this is the condition you used in Chapter 2 of M1. The use of the unit vectors **i** and **j** will not really help you with the type of equilibrium problems in section 2.2 of M1 but you are now able to solve equilibrium problems which are set using the unit vectors, such as the following.

Example 6.3

The system of forces $(2\mathbf{i} + 5\mathbf{j})$ N, $(7\mathbf{i} + Q\,\mathbf{j})$ N, $(P\,\mathbf{i} + 4\mathbf{j})$ N, $(3\mathbf{i} + 8\mathbf{j})$ N acting at a point are in equilibrium. Find P and Q.

The first step is to find the resultant, this is

$$(2\mathbf{i} + 5\mathbf{j} + 7\mathbf{i} + Q\,\mathbf{j} + P\,\mathbf{i} + 4\mathbf{j} + 3\mathbf{i} + 8\mathbf{j})\text{ N} = ((12 + P)\mathbf{i} + (17 + Q)\mathbf{j})\text{ N}.$$

For equilibrium this has to vanish, so $P = -12$, $Q = -17$.

Example 6.4

A system of forces consisting of the following three forces

$(4\mathbf{i} + 20\mathbf{j} + 13\mathbf{k})$ N, $(8\mathbf{i} - 9\mathbf{j} - 3\mathbf{k})$ N, $(4\mathbf{i} + 6\mathbf{j} + 18\mathbf{k})$ N acts at a point.

Find the additional force that has to be included in order that the four forces are in equilibrium.

For equilibrium the sum of the four forces has to be zero. The sum (i.e. the resultant) of the three given forces is $(16\mathbf{i} + 17\mathbf{j} + 28\mathbf{k})$ N. In order that the resultant of the four forces is zero, then the fourth force must be $-(16\mathbf{i} + 17\mathbf{j} + 28\mathbf{k})$ N.

Work done by a constant force

You already know from section 2.1 that the work done by a constant force $\boldsymbol{F}$ when its point of application is moved a distance d is $Fd \cos \theta$, where θ is the angle between $\boldsymbol{F}$ and the direction in which the force is moved. You can use the definition of the scalar product to give the work done as a scalar product. If the point of application of the force is displaced along the vector $\boldsymbol{d}$, then $Fd \cos \theta = \boldsymbol{F}.\boldsymbol{d}$ and so

$$\text{Work done} = \boldsymbol{F}.\boldsymbol{d}.$$

This can be used to find the work done by a force in both two and three dimensions.

<u>**Example 6.5**</u>

Find the work done by (a) the force $(3\mathbf{i} - 8\mathbf{j})$ N when the displacement of its point of application is $(2\mathbf{i} + 6\mathbf{j})$ m, (b) the force $(7\mathbf{i} + 6\mathbf{j} - 3\mathbf{k})$ N when the displacement of its point of application is $(4\mathbf{i} + 8\mathbf{j} - 3\mathbf{k})$ m.

(a) The work done is $(3 \times 2 + (-8) \times 6)$ J $= -42$ J.
(b) The work done is $(7 \times 4 + 6 \times 8 + (-3) \times (-3))$ J $= 85$ J.

<u>**Example 6.6**</u>

The force $(4\mathbf{i} + 8\mathbf{j} - 5\mathbf{k})$ N acts on a particle P, find the work done as P moves from the point (5, 2, 4) m to the point (3, 4, 7) m.

The first step is to find the displacement of P. It is initially at the point with position vector $(5\mathbf{i} + 2\mathbf{j} + 4\mathbf{k})$ m and moves to the point with position vector $(3\mathbf{i} + 4\mathbf{j} + 7\mathbf{k})$ m. The displacement is therefore

$$((3\mathbf{i} + 4\mathbf{j} + 7\mathbf{k}) - (5\mathbf{i} + 2\mathbf{j} + 4\mathbf{k}))\text{ m} = (-2\mathbf{i} + 2\mathbf{j} + 3\mathbf{k})\text{ m}.$$

The work done is therefore

$$(4 \times (-2) + 8 \times 2 + (-5) \times 3)\text{ J} = -7\text{ J}.$$

<u>**Exercises 6.1**</u>

1 Forces $\boldsymbol{P}$ N, $\boldsymbol{Q}$ N and $\boldsymbol{R}$ N act on a particle. Find, in terms of the unit vectors **i**, **j** and **k**, the resultant of these force for the following cases

(a) $\boldsymbol{P} = \mathbf{i} + 3\mathbf{j}$, $\boldsymbol{Q} = 4\mathbf{i} - 2\mathbf{j}$, $\boldsymbol{R} = 11\mathbf{i} - 16\mathbf{j}$.
(b) $\boldsymbol{P} = 7\mathbf{i} - 3\mathbf{j}$, $\boldsymbol{Q} = 3\mathbf{i} + 6\mathbf{j}$, $\boldsymbol{R} = 5\mathbf{i} - 3\mathbf{j}$.
(c) $\boldsymbol{P} = 2\mathbf{i} - 7\mathbf{j} + 6\mathbf{k}$, $\boldsymbol{Q} = 3\mathbf{i} + 14\mathbf{j} - 2\mathbf{k}$, $\boldsymbol{R} = 4\mathbf{i} - \mathbf{j} + 6\mathbf{k}$.
(d) $\boldsymbol{P} = \mathbf{i} + 4\mathbf{j} - 3\mathbf{k}$, $\boldsymbol{Q} = 6\mathbf{i} + 6\mathbf{j} - 12\mathbf{k}$, $\boldsymbol{R} = 3\mathbf{i} + \mathbf{j} + 9\mathbf{k}$.

2 The forces $(4\mathbf{i} + 8\mathbf{j})$ N and $(5\mathbf{i} + 4\mathbf{j})$ N act at a point. Show that their resultant is of magnitude 15 N and find the angle between the forces.

3 Show that the resultant of the forces (3**i** + 6**j** – 3**k**) N and (5**i** – 2**j** – 5**k**) N has magnitude 12 N and find the angles between the forces and between each force and the resultant.

4 The position vectors of two points A and B are (3**i** + 4**j** + 12**k**)m and (2**i** –**j** + 2**k**)m. A force of magnitude 65 N acts along $\overrightarrow{OA}$ and a force of magnitude 12 N acts along $\overrightarrow{OB}$. Find the resultant of these forces.

5 A force of magnitude 15 N acting in the direction of the vector 3**i** + 4**j** is the resultant of two forces acting in the directions of the vectors **i** + 2**j** and 2**i** + **j**. Determine these forces.

6 A particle is in equilibrium under the action of the three forces ***P*** N, ***Q*** N and ***R*** N. Find ***R***, in terms of the unit vectors **i**, **j**, for the following cases

(a) ***P*** = 6**i** – 2**j**, ***Q*** = 3**i** – 5**j**.

(b) ***P*** = – **i** –5**j**, ***Q*** = 11**i** + 4**j**.

(c) ***P*** = 2**i** + 4**j**, ***Q*** = 7**i** – 8**j**.

(d) ***P*** = – **i** – 5**j**, ***Q*** = –2**i** + 11**j**.

7 The displacement of a particle acted on by a force ***F*** N is ***d*** m. Find the work done by the force in this displacement when

(a) ***F*** = 2**i** + 5**j**, ***d*** = 4**i** – 2**j**.

(b) ***F*** = 9**i** – 6**j**, ***d*** = 4**i** – 5**j**.

(c) ***F*** = 3**i** – 4**j** + 2**k**, ***d*** = **i** + 4**j** – **k**.

(d) ***F*** = 2**i** – 3**j** + 2**k**, ***d*** = 4**i** – 6**j** – 5**k**.

8 A particle moves under the action of a force ***F*** N from the point with position vector ***a*** m to the point with position vector ***b*** m. Find the work done when

(a) ***F*** = 4**i** + 2**j**, ***a*** = 3**i** – 4**j**, ***b*** = 6**i** – 8**j**.

(b) ***F*** = 6**i** – 2**j**, ***a*** = 5**i** – 6**j**, ***b*** = 12**i** – 4**j**.

(c) ***F*** = **i** – 6**j** + 4**k**, ***a*** = 4**i** + 7**j** – 12**k**, ***b*** = 2**i** – 4**j** + 3**k**.

(d) ***F*** = 2**i** + **j** – 5**k**, ***a*** = 3**i** + 4**j** – 2**k**, ***b*** = 2**i** + 5**j** + 9**k**.

9 The force acting on a particle is such that

(a) when the displacement of the particle is (3**i** + 4**j**) m the work done by the force is –5 J,

(b) when the displacement of the particle is (7**i** – 8**j**) m the work done by the force is 75 J. Find the force.

6.2 Kinematics

Vectors are particularly useful for describing motion in more than one dimension and use of vector notation gives a direct way of generalising the one dimensional kinematics that you met in M1, Chapter 4.

Velocity, speed and acceleration

The position of a particle is determined by its position vector $\boldsymbol{r}$ relative to a fixed origin and for a moving particle, $\boldsymbol{r}$ will vary with time. The velocity $\boldsymbol{v}$ of a point with position vector $\boldsymbol{r}$ is defined by

$$\boldsymbol{v} = \frac{d\boldsymbol{r}}{dt},$$

i.e. it is the vector whose cartesian components are $\frac{dx}{dt}, \frac{dy}{dt}$ and $\frac{dz}{dt}$. For two dimensional motion (i.e. z = constant) this reduces to the definition you met in section 4.1.

Similarly the acceleration $\boldsymbol{a}$ of a point with position vector $\boldsymbol{r}$ is defined by

$$\boldsymbol{a} = \frac{d\boldsymbol{v}}{dt} = \frac{d^2\boldsymbol{r}}{dt^2},$$

and the cartesian components of acceleration are $\frac{d^2x}{dt^2}, \frac{d^2y}{dt^2}, \frac{d^2z}{dt^2}$.

The speed of a particle is the magnitude of its velocity i.e. speed = v (or $|\boldsymbol{v}|$) and

$$\text{speed} = \sqrt{\left(\frac{dx}{dt}\right)^2 + \left(\frac{dy}{dt}\right)^2 + \left(\frac{dz}{dt}\right)^2}.$$

If the position vector is known, then the velocity and acceleration can be found by differentiation as described in section 5.8. Also the velocity can be found by integrating the acceleration. The integration will involve an arbitrary constant which can be found if the velocity is known for one value of t. Similarly the position vector can be found by integrating the velocity. The integration will again involve an arbitrary constant which can be found if the position vector is known for one value of t. This is just generalising to two and three dimensions the methods that you used in section 4.5 of M1.

<u>Example 6.7</u>

Find the velocity, speed and acceleration of a particle given that at time t s

(a) $\boldsymbol{r} = (4t^2\,\mathbf{i} + 6t^3\,\mathbf{j})$ m, (b) $\boldsymbol{r} = (3\cos 2t\,\mathbf{i} + 3\sin 2t\,\mathbf{j} - 2t\,\mathbf{k})$ m.

(a) Differentiating $\boldsymbol{r}$ gives $\boldsymbol{v} = (8t\,\mathbf{i} + 18t^2\,\mathbf{j})$ ms^{-1} and squaring and adding the components shows that the speed is $\sqrt{64t^2 + 324t^4}$ ms^{-1}.

Differentiating $\boldsymbol{v}$ gives $\boldsymbol{a} = (8\,\mathbf{i} + 36t\,\mathbf{j})$ ms^{-2}.

(b) Differentiating $\boldsymbol{r}$ gives $\boldsymbol{v} = (-6\sin 2t\,\mathbf{i} + 6\cos 2t\,\mathbf{j} - 2\mathbf{k})$ ms^{-1} and squaring and adding the components shows that the speed is

$\sqrt{36\sin^2 2t + 36\cos^2 2t + 4}$ ms^{-1} $= \sqrt{40}$ ms^{-1}.

Differentiating $\boldsymbol{v}$ gives $\boldsymbol{a} = (-12\sin 2t\,\mathbf{i} - 12\cos 2t\,\mathbf{j})$ ms^{-2}.

Example 6.8

Find the velocity and position vector, given that

(a) $\boldsymbol{a} = (12t\,\mathbf{i} + 80t^3\,\mathbf{j})$ ms^{-2}, and that at $t = 0$, $\boldsymbol{v} = (3\mathbf{i} + 7\mathbf{j})$ ms^{-1}, $\boldsymbol{r} = (2\mathbf{i} + 11\mathbf{j})$ m,

(b) $\boldsymbol{a} = (6\mathbf{i} + 7\mathrm{e}^{-t}\,\mathbf{j} + \cos t\,\mathbf{k})$ ms^{-2}, and that at $t = 0$, $\boldsymbol{v} = (\mathbf{i} + 4\mathbf{j} + 3\mathbf{k})$ ms^{-1},

$\boldsymbol{r} = (3\mathbf{i} + \mathbf{j} - 2\mathbf{k})$ m.

(a) Integrating the acceleration gives $\boldsymbol{v} = (6t^2\,\mathbf{i} + 20t^4\,\mathbf{j} + \boldsymbol{b})$ ms^{-1}, where $\boldsymbol{b}$ is a constant vector. Substituting the values at $t = 0$ gives $3\mathbf{i} + 7\mathbf{j} = \boldsymbol{b}$ so that

$$\boldsymbol{v} = ((6t^2 + 3)\mathbf{i} + (20t^4 + 7)\mathbf{j})\text{ ms}^{-1}.$$

Integrating again gives

$$\boldsymbol{r} = ((3t^3 + 3t)\mathbf{i} + (4t^5 + 7t)\mathbf{j} + \boldsymbol{c})\text{ m, where } \boldsymbol{c} \text{ is a constant vector.}$$

Substituting the values at $t = 0$ gives $2\mathbf{i} + 11\mathbf{j} = \boldsymbol{c}$ so that

$$\boldsymbol{r} = ((3t^3 + 3t + 2)\mathbf{i} + (4t^5 + 7t + 11)\mathbf{j})\text{ m.}$$

(b) Integrating the acceleration gives $\boldsymbol{v} = (6t\,\mathbf{i} - 7\mathrm{e}^{-t}\,\mathbf{j} + \sin t\,\mathbf{k} + \boldsymbol{b})$ ms^{-1}, where $\boldsymbol{b}$ is a constant vector. Substituting the values at $t = 0$ gives

$$\mathbf{i} + 4\mathbf{j} + 3\mathbf{k} = -7\mathbf{j} + \boldsymbol{b} \text{ so that } \boldsymbol{b} = \mathbf{i} + 11\mathbf{j} + 3\mathbf{k} \text{ and}$$

$$\boldsymbol{v} = ((6t + 1)\mathbf{i} + (11 - 7\mathrm{e}^{-t})\mathbf{j} + (3 + \sin t)\mathbf{k})\text{ ms}^{-1}.$$

Integrating again gives

$$\boldsymbol{r} = ((3t^2 + t)\mathbf{i} + (11t + 7\mathrm{e}^{-t})\mathbf{j} + (3t - \cos t)\mathbf{k} + \boldsymbol{c})\text{ m,}$$

where $\boldsymbol{c}$ is a constant vector. Substituting the values at $t = 0$ gives

$$3\mathbf{i} + \mathbf{j} - 2\,\mathbf{k} = 7\mathbf{j} - \mathbf{k} + \boldsymbol{c} \text{ so that } \boldsymbol{c} = 3\mathbf{i} - 6\mathbf{j} - \mathbf{k} \text{ and}$$

$$\boldsymbol{r} = ((3t^2 + t + 3)\mathbf{i} + (11t - 6 + 7\mathrm{e}^{-t})\mathbf{j} + (3t - 1 - \cos t)\mathbf{k})\text{ m.}$$

An alternative to introducing the constant vectors would have been to integrate each time from $t = 0$ to $t = t$. You should try to re-do the example by doing this.

Interception and shortest distance problems

There are many problems of a practical type involving determining the shortest distance apart of two moving bodies (e.g. aircraft) or whether they intercept each other. In order to do this the displacement of the bodies from each other and the least magnitude of this, or the condition for interception, can be found. The displacement can be obtained from the position vectors of the bodies. These may either be given or the velocity or acceleration given. The position vector can then be found by integration as above. The problems that can be most easily tackled are those when the bodies are moving with constant velocity. If a particle has a constant velocity $\boldsymbol{V}$ then

$$\frac{\mathrm{d}\boldsymbol{r}}{\mathrm{d}t} = \boldsymbol{V}$$

and integrating gives $\boldsymbol{r} = \boldsymbol{V}t + \boldsymbol{b}$ where $\boldsymbol{b}$ is a constant vector. If the particle has position vector $\boldsymbol{a}$ for $t = 0$ it follows that $\boldsymbol{b} = \boldsymbol{a}$ so that $\boldsymbol{r} = \boldsymbol{V}t + \boldsymbol{a}$.

Example 6.9

At time $t = 0$ two particles A and B have position vectors $(5\mathbf{i} + 3\mathbf{j})$ m and $(\mathbf{i} + \mathbf{j})$ m respectively. The velocities of A and B are $(6\mathbf{i} + 4\mathbf{j})$ ms^{-1} and $(8\mathbf{i} + 5\mathbf{j})$ ms^{-1} respectively. Show that the particles will collide.

The first step is to find the position vectors $\boldsymbol{r}_A$ m and $\boldsymbol{r}_B$ m of the particles at time t s. These are, from the above result that $\boldsymbol{r} = \boldsymbol{V}t + \boldsymbol{a}$,

$$\boldsymbol{r}_A = 5\mathbf{i} + 3\mathbf{j} + t(6\mathbf{i} + 4\mathbf{j}), \qquad \boldsymbol{r}_B = \mathbf{i} + \mathbf{j} + t(8\mathbf{i} + 5\mathbf{j}).$$

Subtracting these gives

$$\overrightarrow{AB} = -4\mathbf{i} - 2\mathbf{j} + t(2\mathbf{i} + \mathbf{j}).$$

For interception, both components have to vanish and this occurs for $t = 2$.

Example 6.10

At time $t = 0$, two particles A and B have position vectors $(3\mathbf{i} + 6\mathbf{k})$ m and $(2\mathbf{i} + a\mathbf{j} + 2\mathbf{k})$ m respectively. The velocities of A and B are $(3\mathbf{j} + 7\mathbf{k})$ ms^{-1} and $(b\mathbf{i} + 6\mathbf{j} + 11\mathbf{k})$ ms^{-1} respectively. Find the values of a and b so that the particles collide.

The position vectors $\boldsymbol{r}_A$ m and $\boldsymbol{r}_B$ m of the particles at time t s are given, using $\boldsymbol{r} = \boldsymbol{V}t + \boldsymbol{a}$, by $\boldsymbol{r}_A = 3\mathbf{i} + 6\mathbf{k} + t(3\mathbf{j} + 7\mathbf{k})$, $\boldsymbol{r}_B = 2\mathbf{i} + a\mathbf{j} + 2\mathbf{k} + t(b\mathbf{i} + 6\mathbf{j} + 11\mathbf{k})$.

Subtracting these gives

$$\begin{aligned}\overrightarrow{AB} &= -\mathbf{i} + a\mathbf{j} - 4\mathbf{k} + t(b\mathbf{i} + 3\mathbf{j} + 4\mathbf{k}), \\ &= (bt - 1)\mathbf{i} + (a + 3t)\mathbf{j} + 4(t - 1)\mathbf{k}.\end{aligned}$$

For interception all components have to vanish, the $\mathbf{k}$ component vanishes for $t = 1$ and the $\mathbf{j}$ and $\mathbf{i}$ components are then $3 + a$ and $b - 1$. Collision therefore occurs for $b = 1$ and $a = -3$.

Example 6.11

At time $t = 0$ two particles A and B have position vectors $(11\mathbf{i} + 7\mathbf{j})$ m and $(3\mathbf{i} + 5\mathbf{j})$ m respectively. The velocities of A and B are $(2\mathbf{i} + 3\mathbf{j})$ ms^{-1} and $(5\mathbf{i} + 7\mathbf{j})$ ms^{-1} respectively. Determine when the particles will be nearest to each other and find their shortest distance apart.

The position vectors $\boldsymbol{r}_A$ m and $\boldsymbol{r}_B$ m of the particles at time t s are

$$\boldsymbol{r}_A = 11\mathbf{i} + 7\mathbf{j} + t(2\mathbf{i} + 3\mathbf{j}), \qquad \boldsymbol{r}_B = 3\mathbf{i} + 5\mathbf{j} + t(5\mathbf{i} + 7\mathbf{j}).$$

Subtracting these gives

$$\begin{aligned}\overrightarrow{AB} &= -8\mathbf{i} - 2\mathbf{j} + t(3\mathbf{i} + 4\mathbf{j}), \\ &= (3t - 8)\mathbf{i} + (4t - 2)\mathbf{j}.\end{aligned}$$

Therefore AB^2, the square of their distance apart, is given by

$$AB^2 = (3t-8)^2 + (4t-2)^2.$$

The minimum value of this has now to be found. This can be done by use of calculus or by expanding out and completing the square. Use of calculus involves slightly less algebra and it is not necessary to expand out before differentiating.

$$\frac{\mathrm{d}AB^2}{\mathrm{d}t} = 6(3t-8) + 8(4t-2) = 50t - 64 = 0.$$

Therefore $t = 1.28$ and the shortest distance apart is 5.2 m.

It is not necessary to check that you have a minimum value since AB^2 tends to infinity with both negative and positive t, therefore plotted against t it would be a parabola with its vertex downwards and therefore the stationary point is a minimum.

Example 6.12

The position vectors at time $t = 0$ of two particles A and B are $(5\mathbf{i} + 7\mathbf{j} + 6\mathbf{k})$ m and $(3\mathbf{i} + 2\mathbf{j} + 3\mathbf{k})$ m respectively. The velocities of A and B are $(\mathbf{i} + 2\mathbf{j} + 4\mathbf{k})$ ms^{-1} and $(3\mathbf{i} + 4\mathbf{j} + 7\mathbf{k})$ ms^{-1} respectively. Find the value of t when the particles are nearest to each other and their shortest distance of approach.

The position vectors $\boldsymbol{r}_A$ m and $\boldsymbol{r}_B$ m of the particles at time t s are given by

$$\boldsymbol{r}_A = 5\mathbf{i} + 7\mathbf{j} + 6\mathbf{k} + t(\mathbf{i} + 2\mathbf{j} + 4\mathbf{k}),$$

$$\boldsymbol{r}_B = 3\mathbf{i} + 2\mathbf{j} + 3\mathbf{k} + t(3\mathbf{i} + 4\mathbf{j} + 7\mathbf{k}).$$

Subtracting these gives

$$\overrightarrow{AB} = -2\mathbf{i} - 5\mathbf{j} - 3\mathbf{k} + t(2\mathbf{i} + 2\mathbf{j} + 3\mathbf{k})$$

$$= (2t-2)\mathbf{i} + (2t-5)\mathbf{j} + (3t-3)\mathbf{k}.$$

Therefore AB^2, the square of their distance apart, is given by

$$AB^2 = (2t-2)^2 + (2t-5)^2 + (3t-3)^2.$$

Differentiating gives

$$\frac{\mathrm{d}AB^2}{\mathrm{d}t} = 4(2t-2) + 4(2t-5) + 6(3t-3) = 34t - 46 = 0.$$

Therefore $t = 1.35$ and the shortest distance of approach is 2.62 m.

Resultant velocity

There are some circumstances where the motion of a particle is the result of two or more independent causes. One example is rain falling down. In this case the motion of the rain drop can be viewed as the superposition of a falling motion and a motion due to the wind. There will be a velocity from each cause and the actual, i.e. resultant, velocity will be the vector sum of the individual velocities. Another example is an aircraft which sets off on a particular course with a given velocity. If there is a wind, the actual velocity of the aircraft is the resultant of the velocity on its set course and the wind velocity. It will therefore drift well off course and a pilot normally adjusts the set course to take the effect of the wind into account.

Example 6.13

A river, 40 m wide, flows from west to east with speed 4 ms^{-1}. A motor boat seeking to cross the river from the southern bank moves with speed 6 ms^{-1} in still water. The boat is steered perpendicular to the banks so that its actual velocity is the resultant of the velocity of the river and a velocity of 6 ms^{-1} directly across the river. Find how far down river the boat lands.

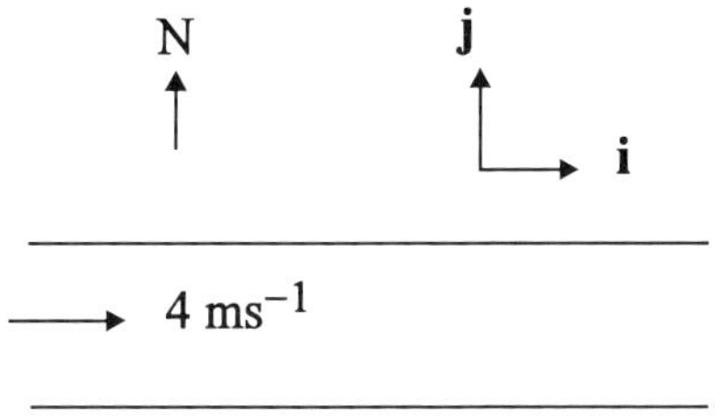

The situation is shown in the diagram, where **i** denotes the unit vector from west to east and **j** denotes the unit vector from south to north. The velocity of 6 ms^{-1} directly across is 6**j** ms^{-1}. The velocity of the boat is therefore the resultant of 6**j** ms^{-1} and 4**i** ms^{-1} and is (4**i** + 6**j**) ms^{-1}. At time t s after leaving the starting point, the displacement of the boat from the starting point is (4**i** + 6**j**)t m. The boat will have reached the opposite bank when the **j** component of the displacement is 40 m and therefore the time taken to cross is $\frac{40}{6}$ s = 6.67 s.

The distance down river of the landing place is the **i** component of the displacement and is therefore 4×6.67 m $= 26.7$ m.

Example 6.14

An aircraft sets off to fly directly east with speed 400 kmh^{-1} so as to reach a destination 1600 km away in 4 hours. There is a wind of 75 kmh^{-1} blowing from the south east.

(a) If the pilot does not adjust the course, determine the distance of the aircraft from its destination after 4 hours flying.

(b) Determine the course that the pilot would have to set so as to fly directly to the initial destination and the flight time.

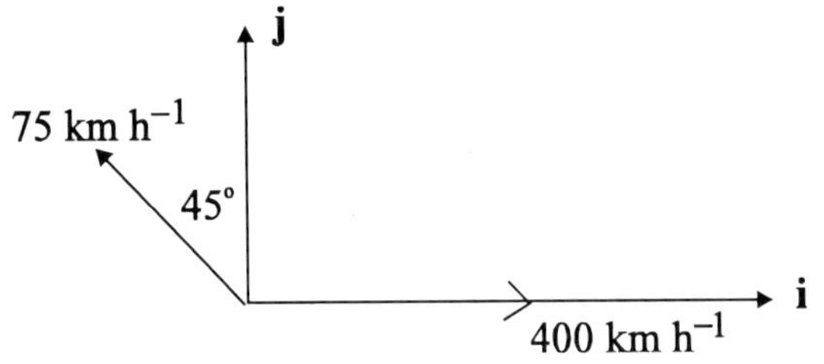

(a) In this question there are no unit vectors given and the first step is to choose appropriate ones. The diagram shows unit vectors **i** and **j** to the east and north respectively. The velocity of the aircraft on its set course to the east is 400 **i** km h^{-1}. The wind velocity is 75(−cos 45°**i** + sin 45°**j**) kmh^{-1}. The resultant velocity of the aircraft is therefore ((400 − 75 cos 45°)**i** + 75 sin 45°**j**) kmh^{-1}. In four hours its displacement from its original position will therefore be 4 × ((400 − 75 cos 45°)**i** + 75 sin 45°**j**) km. The displacement of the destination from the starting point is 1600**i** km and therefore the displacement of the aircraft from its destination is
{4 × ((400 − 75 cos 45°)**i** + 75 sin 45°**j**) − 1600**i**} km = 300(− cos 45°**i** + sin 45°**j**) km. The magnitude of this is approximately 424 km.

(b)

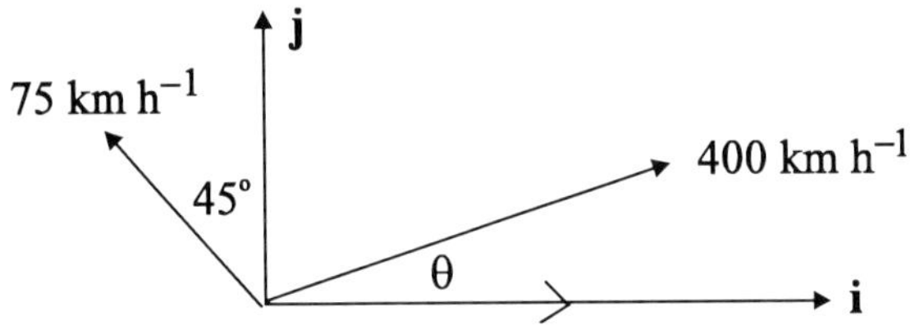

In this case the set course of the aircraft is unknown and it is assumed, as in the diagram, to be at an angle θ north of east. Since there is a component of the wind to the north it would appear that the aircraft will be blown further off course. However θ does not have to be positive and in fact turns out to be negative. A negative sign could therefore be avoided by using common sense and assuming that the set course would be to the south of east! The velocity of the aircraft on its set course is therefore

$$400(\cos\theta\,\mathbf{i} + \sin\theta\,\mathbf{j})\ \text{kmh}^{-1}.$$

The resultant velocity is therefore

$$((400\cos\theta - 75\cos 45°)\,\mathbf{i} + (400\sin\theta + 75\cos 45°)\,\mathbf{j}\,)\ \text{kmh}^{-1}.$$

The resultant velocity has to be to the east and therefore

$$400\sin\theta + 75\cos 45° = 0,$$

giving θ = −7.6°, with the negative sign anticipated. Substituting for θ gives the resultant velocity as 343 kmh^{-1} to the east and the flight time is therefore 4.66 hours.

Exercises 6.2

1 The position vector at time t s of a moving particle is $\boldsymbol{r}$ m. Find the acceleration of the particle for the cases (a) $\boldsymbol{r} = 7t^3\ \mathbf{i} + 4t^2\ \mathbf{j}$, (b) $\boldsymbol{r} = 4e^{-t}\mathbf{i} + 2e^{2t}\mathbf{j}$, (c) $\boldsymbol{r} = t\,\mathbf{i} - 8t^2\ \mathbf{j} + 14t^3\mathbf{k}$ (d) $\boldsymbol{r} = e^{4t}\ \mathbf{i} - 8e^{t}\ \mathbf{j} + 14\cos t\ \mathbf{k}$.

2 The velocity of a particle at time t s is $(6t^2\ \mathbf{i} + 10t\ \mathbf{j})$ ms^{-1} and it is at the point O when $t = 0$. Find its displacement from O when $t = 3$.

3 The acceleration of a particle at time t s is $(5t^4\ \mathbf{i} - 8t^3\ \mathbf{j})$ ms^{-2} and its velocity is $(6\mathbf{i} - 5\mathbf{j})$ ms^{-1} when $t = 1$. Find the velocity of the particle when $t = 2$.

4 At $t = 0$ a particle P is at rest at the point with position vector $(3\mathbf{i} + 4\mathbf{j} - 3\mathbf{k})$ m relative to a fixed point O. The acceleration of the particle is $(2t\ \mathbf{i} + 12t^2\ \mathbf{j} - 16t^3\mathbf{k})$ ms^{-2}. Find the distance of the particle from O when $t = 1$.

5 The acceleration of a particle at time t s is $(2\mathbf{i} + 4t\ \mathbf{j} - 6t^2\ \mathbf{k})$ ms^{-2} and its velocity is $(3\mathbf{i} + 5\mathbf{j} + 2\mathbf{k})$ ms^{-1} when $t = 1$. Find the speed of the particle when $t = 2$.

6 At time t s a particle is moving with velocity $(2\mathbf{i} + 6\mathbf{j} - 4t^3\mathbf{k})$ ms^{-1} and at time $t = 0$ it is at the point with position vector $(\mathbf{i} - 3\mathbf{j} + 2\mathbf{k})$ m. Find the distance between the positions of the particle at $t = 1$ and $t = 2$.

7 At noon the position vectors, relative to a fixed point, of two boats A and B are $(900\mathbf{i} + 600\mathbf{j})$ m and $(600\mathbf{i} + 810\mathbf{j})$ m respectively, where $\mathbf{i}$ and $\mathbf{j}$ are unit vectors to the north and east respectively. The velocity of boat A is $(12\mathbf{i} + 16\mathbf{j})$ ms^{-1} whilst that of boat B is $(15\mathbf{i} + 10\mathbf{j})$ ms^{-1}. Find (a) the vector $\overrightarrow{AB}$ at time t s after noon, (b) the time when the two boats are nearest to each other and their shortest distance apart.

8 A destroyer sights a ship at a point with position vector $600(3\mathbf{i} + \mathbf{j})$ m relative to it and moving with velocity $5\mathbf{j}$ ms^{-1}. The destroyer alters course so that it moves with speed v ms^{-1} in the direction of the vector $4\mathbf{i} + 3\mathbf{j}$. Find v so that the destroyer intercepts the ship and the time to interception.

9 The velocities of two particles A and B are $(4\mathbf{i} + 3\mathbf{j} + 2\mathbf{k})$ ms^{-1} and $(2\mathbf{i} - \mathbf{j} + 4\mathbf{k})$ ms^{-1} respectively. At a particular instant the position vector of B relative to A is $(8\mathbf{i} + 16\mathbf{j} - 8\mathbf{k})$ m. Show that the particles will collide.

10 The velocities of two aircraft A and B are $(210\mathbf{i} - 50\mathbf{j})$ kmh^{-1} and $(150\mathbf{i} + 250\mathbf{j} + 60\mathbf{k})$ kmh^{-1} respectively. At a particular instant the position vectors of A and B relative to a control tower are $(10\mathbf{i} + 20\mathbf{j} + 5\mathbf{k})$ km and $(-20\mathbf{i} - 10\mathbf{j} + 3\mathbf{k})$ km.
Find the vector $\overrightarrow{AB}$ at time t hours later and the time taken until the aircrafts are closest together.

11 An aircraft flies due south at 280kmh^{-1} in a crosswind blowing west at 25kmh^{-1}. Find the resultant velocity of the aircraft.

12 A boat is sailing at a speed of 2 ms^{-1} due west in a current flowing north east at a rate of 1 ms^{-1}. Find the resultant velocity of the boat.

13 A man, who can swim at a speed of 2 ms^{-1} in still water, wants to swim straight across to the other side of a river which is 20 m across. The river is flowing with speed 1.25 ms^{-1}. Find the angle to the bank at which he should swim and the time he takes to cross.

6.3 Dynamics

Vector notation gives a compact way of stating Newton's second law (i.e. force = mass × acceleration). The equation of motion, under the action of a force $\boldsymbol{F}$, of a particle of mass m is

$$m\frac{d^2\mathbf{r}}{dt^2} = \boldsymbol{F},$$

where $\boldsymbol{r}$ denotes the position vector of the particle. If, for a moving particle, $\boldsymbol{r}$ can be found by observation, then the acceleration can be found by differentiation and this would enable the force producing the motion to be determined from the equation of motion. Alternatively if the force is given, then the equation of motion could be used to find $\boldsymbol{r}$. If $\boldsymbol{F}$ is given in terms of t then $\boldsymbol{r}$ can be found by integration as in section 5.8. A particularly simple case of this is when the force (and therefore the acceleration) is constant.

Motion under constant force

If $\boldsymbol{F}$ is constant, then the above equation can be integrated directly using rule (vii) of section 5.8 and this gives

$$m\frac{\mathrm{d}\boldsymbol{r}}{\mathrm{d}t} = \boldsymbol{F}t + \boldsymbol{c},$$

where $\boldsymbol{c}$ is a constant vector. If the velocity (i.e. $\frac{\mathrm{d}\boldsymbol{r}}{\mathrm{d}t}$) is equal to $\boldsymbol{v}$ at $t = 0$ then substituting gives $\boldsymbol{c} = m\boldsymbol{v}$. Integrating again gives

$$m\boldsymbol{r} = \frac{1}{2}\boldsymbol{F}t^2 + m\boldsymbol{v}t + \boldsymbol{b},$$

where $\boldsymbol{b}$ is a constant vector. If the particle is at the point with position vector $\boldsymbol{R}$ at $t = 0$ then substituting $\boldsymbol{r} = \boldsymbol{R}$ and $t = 0$ gives $\boldsymbol{b} = m\boldsymbol{R}$. Therefore $\boldsymbol{r}$ is given by

$$\boldsymbol{r} = \frac{\boldsymbol{F}}{2m}t^2 + \boldsymbol{v}t + \boldsymbol{R}.$$

This result can be applied to the motion of a particle under gravity where $\boldsymbol{F} = -mg\mathbf{j}$, where $\mathbf{j}$ is the unit vector vertically upwards. If a particle is projected with speed V at an angle α to the horizontal, then $\boldsymbol{v} = V\cos\alpha\,\mathbf{i} + V\sin\alpha\,\mathbf{j}$, where $\mathbf{i}$ is a horizontal unit vector. Therefore for a particle projected from the origin (so that $\boldsymbol{R} = \boldsymbol{0}$)

$$\boldsymbol{r} = -\frac{1}{2}gt^2\,\mathbf{j} + V(\cos\alpha\,\mathbf{i} + \sin\alpha\,\mathbf{j})t.$$

Since $\boldsymbol{r} = x\,\mathbf{i} + y\,\mathbf{j}$, these are the equations that were previously obtained in section 5.2 The equations of motion can be integrated in a similar fashion whenever the force is dependent only on t.

Example 6.15

At time t s the position vector of a moving particle of mass 0.3 kg is $(7t^2\,\mathbf{i} + 3t^4\,\mathbf{j} + 2t^3\,\mathbf{k})$ m. Find the force acting on the particle.

To find the force, it is necessary to find the acceleration. Differentiating the position vector once gives the velocity as $(14t\,\mathbf{i} + 12t^3\mathbf{j} + 6t^2\,\mathbf{k})$ ms^{-1}, and differentiating the velocity gives the acceleration as $(14\mathbf{i} + 36t^2\,\mathbf{j} + 12t\,\mathbf{k})$ ms^{-2}. Multiplying this by 0.3 gives the force as $(4.2\mathbf{i} + 10.8t^2\,\mathbf{j} + 3.6t\,\mathbf{k})$ N.

Example 6.16

A particle of mass 0.25 kg moves under the action of a force which at time t s is given by $(3t\mathbf{i} + 2\mathbf{j} + 10t^3\mathbf{k})$ N. At $t = 0$ the particle is at the point with position vector $(2\mathbf{i} + 5\mathbf{j} - 7\mathbf{k})$ m and moving with velocity $(\mathbf{i} - 4\mathbf{j} + 3\mathbf{k})$ ms^{-1}. Find the position vector in terms of t.

The equation of motion is

$$0.25\,\frac{d^2\mathbf{r}}{dt^2} = 3t\,\mathbf{i} + 2\mathbf{j} + 10t^3\,\mathbf{k},$$

where the position vector is denoted by $\boldsymbol{r}$ m, therefore

$$\frac{d^2\mathbf{r}}{dt^2} = 12t\,\mathbf{i} + 8\mathbf{j} + 40t^3\,\mathbf{k}.$$

Integrating this gives $\quad \dfrac{\mathrm{d}\boldsymbol{r}}{\mathrm{d}t} = 6t^2\,\mathbf{i} + 8t\,\mathbf{j} + 10t^4\,\mathbf{k} + \boldsymbol{c},$

where $\boldsymbol{c}$ is a constant vector. Substituting $\dfrac{\mathrm{d}\boldsymbol{r}}{\mathrm{d}t} = \mathbf{i} - 4\mathbf{j} + 3\mathbf{k}$ for $t = 0$ shows that

$$\boldsymbol{c} = \mathbf{i} - 4\mathbf{j} + 3\mathbf{k}.$$

Integrating for a second time gives

$$\boldsymbol{r} = 2t^3\,\mathbf{i} + 4t^2\,\mathbf{j} + 2t^5\,\mathbf{k} + (\mathbf{i} - 4\mathbf{j} + 3\mathbf{k})t + \boldsymbol{b},$$

where $\boldsymbol{b}$ is a constant vector. Substituting $t = 0$ into the expression for $\boldsymbol{r}$ and using the given position vector at $t = 0$ shows that $\boldsymbol{b} = 2\mathbf{i} + 5\mathbf{j} - 7\mathbf{k}$.

Example 6.17

The force acting on a particle at time t s is $(36t^2\,\mathbf{i} + 120t^4\,\mathbf{j} + 24\mathbf{k})$ N. The particle is at rest at O at time $t = 0$ and when $t = 1$ the particle is at a distance of 26 m from O. Find the mass of the particle.

If the mass of the particle is denoted by m kg, and its position vector by $\boldsymbol{r}$ m, then Newton's law gives

$$m\,\frac{d^2\boldsymbol{r}}{dt^2} = 36t^2\ \mathbf{i} + 120t^4\ \mathbf{j} + 24\mathbf{k}.$$

Integrating this equation gives

$$m\,\frac{\mathrm{d}\boldsymbol{r}}{\mathrm{d}t} = 12t^3\ \mathbf{i} + 24t^5\ \mathbf{j} + 24t\ \mathbf{k} + \boldsymbol{b},$$

where $\boldsymbol{b}$ is a constant vector. Since the velocity is zero at $t = 0$ it follows that $\boldsymbol{b} = \mathbf{0}$.

Integrating again gives

$$m\boldsymbol{r} = 3t^4\ \mathbf{i} + 4t^6\ \mathbf{j} + 12t^2\ \mathbf{k} + \boldsymbol{c},$$

where $\boldsymbol{c}$ is a constant vector. Since $\boldsymbol{r} = \mathbf{0}$ at $t = 0$ it follows that $\boldsymbol{c} = \mathbf{0}$.

Therefore for $t = 1$

$$\boldsymbol{r} = \frac{1}{m}(3\mathbf{i} + 4\mathbf{j} + 12\mathbf{k}).$$

Therefore

$$r = \frac{1}{m}\sqrt{3^2 + 4^2 + 12^2} = \frac{13}{m} = 26,$$

and therefore the mass of the particle is 0.5 kg.

Vector notation also enables the ideas of impulse, momentum, power and energy to be generalised to two and three dimensional motion.

Momentum and impulse

The momentum of a particle of mass m is defined as the product of the mass and velocity i.e.

$$\text{Momentum} = m\,\boldsymbol{v} = m\frac{\mathrm{d}\boldsymbol{r}}{\mathrm{d}t}.$$

Momentum is therefore a vector.

Impulse is also defined in essentially the same way as in one dimension as the integral of a force. The impulse of a force $\boldsymbol{F}$ acting for time T is defined by

$$\text{Impulse} = \int_0^T \boldsymbol{F}\,\mathrm{d}t.$$

Impulse is therefore also a vector.

If the force is constant, then the integral becomes $\boldsymbol{F}T$ i.e. the impulse of a constant force is the product of the force and the time for which it acts.

Example 6.18

Find the impulse of (a) the force $[(2t\,\mathbf{i} + 5t^4\,\mathbf{j})]$ N acting for $0 \le t \le 1$,
(b) the force $(4\mathbf{i} - 3t^2\,\mathbf{j} + 6t\,\mathbf{k})$ N acting for $0 \le t \le 2$.

(a) Impulse $= \int_0^1 (2t\,\mathbf{i} + 5t^4\mathbf{j})\,\mathrm{d}t$ Ns $= [(t^2\,\mathbf{i} + t^5\mathbf{j})]_{t=0}^{t=1}$ Ns $= (\mathbf{i} + \mathbf{j})$ Ns.

(b) Impulse $= \int_0^2 (4\mathbf{i} - 3t^2\mathbf{j} + 6t\,\mathbf{k})\,\mathrm{d}t$ Ns $= (8\mathbf{i} - 8\mathbf{j} + 12\mathbf{k})$ Ns.

Impulse momentum principle

Integrating

$$m\frac{d^2\boldsymbol{r}}{dt^2} = \boldsymbol{F},$$

from $t = 0$ to $t = T$ gives

$$\left(m\frac{\mathrm{d}\boldsymbol{r}}{\mathrm{d}t}\right)_{t=T} - \left(m\frac{\mathrm{d}\boldsymbol{r}}{\mathrm{d}t}\right)_{t=0} = \int_0^T \boldsymbol{F}\mathrm{d}t\,.$$

The left hand side is the change in momentum from $t = 0$ to $t = T$ and the right hand side is the impulse. Therefore the above definitions ensure that the impulse momentum principle still holds for two and three dimensional motion.

Example 6.19

A particle of mass 0.3 kg, moving with velocity $(2\mathbf{i} + 8\mathbf{j})$ ms^{-1}, is struck a sharp blow which changes its velocity to $(4\mathbf{i} + 5\mathbf{j})$ ms^{-1}. Find the impulse applied during the blow.

The impulse is equal to the change of momentum and is

$$0.3(4\mathbf{i} + 5\mathbf{j} - 2\mathbf{i} - 8\mathbf{j})\text{ Ns} = (0.6\mathbf{i} - 0.9\mathbf{j})\text{ Ns}.$$

Example 6.20

An impulse $(6\mathbf{i} + 5\mathbf{j} - 16\mathbf{k})$ Ns is applied to a particle of mass 0.25 kg moving with velocity $(2\mathbf{i} - 4\mathbf{j} + 7\mathbf{k})$ ms^{-1}. Find the velocity of the particle after the impulse has been applied.

If the required velocity is denoted by $\boldsymbol{v}$ ms^{-1} then the impulse momentum principle gives

$$0.25(\boldsymbol{v} - 2\mathbf{i} + 4\mathbf{j} - 7\mathbf{k}) = 6\mathbf{i} + 5\mathbf{j} - 16\mathbf{k}$$

and therefore

$$\boldsymbol{v} = 26\mathbf{i} + 16\mathbf{j} - 57\mathbf{k}.$$

Kinetic energy

Kinetic energy is defined, exactly as in one dimension, as one half the product of the mass and the square of the speed. Therefore the kinetic energy of a particle of mass m moving with velocity $\boldsymbol{v}$ is given by

$$\text{Kinetic Energy} = \frac{1}{2}mv^2 \text{ (i.e. } \frac{1}{2}m\,|\,\boldsymbol{v}\,|^2\text{).}$$

Example 6.21

Find the kinetic energy of a particle of mass 0.2 kg moving with velocity $(2\mathbf{i} + 4\mathbf{j} - 7\mathbf{k})$ ms $^{-1}$.

The kinetic energy is

$$\frac{1}{2} \times 0.2 \times (2^2 + 4^2 + 7^2)\text{ J} = 6.9\text{ J.}$$

Example 6.22

Find the kinetic energy of a particle of mass 0.4 kg moving at time t s with velocity $(4t\,\mathbf{i} + 5t^2\,\mathbf{j} - 7t^3\,\mathbf{k})$ ms $^{-1}$ ·

The speed squared is the sum of the squares of the components and so kinetic energy is

$$\frac{1}{2} \times 0.4\,(16^2 + 25t^4 + 49t^6)\text{ J} = (3.2t^2 + 5t^4 + 9.8t^6)\text{ J.}$$

Example 6.23

Find the kinetic energy of a particle of mass 0.8 kg whose position vector at time t s is $(6t\,\mathbf{i} + 4t^2\,\mathbf{j} - 7\cos t\,\mathbf{k})$ m.

The first step is to differentiate the position vector to find the velocity, this gives the velocity to be $(6\mathbf{i} + 8t\,\mathbf{j} + 7\sin t\,\mathbf{k})$ ms $^{-1}$. The kinetic energy is therefore

$$\frac{1}{2} \times 0.8\,(36 + 64t^2 + 49\sin^2 t)\text{ J} = (14.4 + 25.6t^2 + 19.6\sin^2 t)\text{ J.}$$

Power

The generalisation of the definition of power is that the power developed by a force $\boldsymbol{F}$ when its point of application is moving with velocity $\boldsymbol{v}$ is given by

$$\text{Power} = \boldsymbol{F} \,.\, \boldsymbol{v}.$$

Power defined this way is still the rate of doing work. Defining work done in more than one dimension needs more pure mathematics than will be covered in your course and therefore you cannot verify that the definition does give power as the rate of working.

Since power is the rate of doing work, then integrating the power between two values of t will give the total work done in that time interval.

Example 6.24

At time t s the position vector of a moving particle is $(4t\,\mathbf{i} + 0.6t^2\,\mathbf{j} - 0.25(t^3 - 1)\mathbf{k})$ m. Find the power developed for $t = 4$ by the force $(10\mathbf{i} - 20\mathbf{j} - 20\mathbf{k})$ N acting on the particle.

The velocity of the particle and therefore of the point of application of the force is $(4\mathbf{i} + 1.2t\,\mathbf{j} - 0.75t^2\,\mathbf{k})$ ms^{-1}. The power is the scalar product of the velocity and the force and is therefore $(10 \times 4 - 20 \times 1.2t + 15t^2)$ W. This, for $t = 4$, is equal to 184 W.

Example 6.25

Find the power developed by the force in Example 5.22.

The first step is calculating the force and this, in turn, means finding the acceleration. Differentiating the velocity gives the acceleration to be $(4\mathbf{i} + 10\,\mathbf{j} - 21t^2\,\mathbf{k})$ ms^{-2} and therefore the force is

$$0.4 \times (4\mathbf{i} + 10t\,\mathbf{j} - 21t^2\,\mathbf{k})\text{ N} = (1.6\mathbf{i} + 4t\,\mathbf{j} - 8.4t^2\,\mathbf{k})\text{ N}.$$

Therefore the power is

$$(1.6 \times 4t + 4t \times 5t^2 + (-8.4\,t^2) \times (-7t^3))\text{ W} = (6.4t + 20t^3 + 58.8t^5)\text{ W}.$$

Work- energy principle

Newton's second law, for a particle of mass m moving with velocity $\boldsymbol{v}$ under the action of a force $\boldsymbol{F}$, is

$$m\frac{\mathrm{d}\boldsymbol{v}}{\mathrm{d}t} = \boldsymbol{F}.$$

Taking the scalar product of both sides of this equation with $\boldsymbol{v}$ gives

$$m\boldsymbol{v}\cdot\frac{\mathrm{d}\boldsymbol{v}}{\mathrm{d}t} = \boldsymbol{F}\cdot\boldsymbol{v}.$$

The rule for differentiating the scalar product shows that

$$\boldsymbol{v}\cdot\frac{\mathrm{d}\boldsymbol{v}}{\mathrm{d}t} = \frac{\mathrm{d}\left(\frac{1}{2}\boldsymbol{v}\cdot\boldsymbol{v}\right)}{\mathrm{d}t} = \frac{\mathrm{d}\left(\frac{1}{2}v^2\right)}{\mathrm{d}t}.$$

Using this identity in the previous equation gives

$$m\frac{\mathrm{d}\left(\frac{1}{2}v^2\right)}{\mathrm{d}t} = \boldsymbol{F}\cdot\boldsymbol{v}.$$

This equation translated into words is

Rate of change of kinetic energy = power.

You can see that differentiating the kinetic energy in Example 5.22 gives the power found in Example 5.25. Since power is the rate of doing work, W, the equation can also be written as

$$\frac{\mathrm{d(K.E.)}}{\mathrm{d}t} = \frac{\mathrm{d}W}{\mathrm{d}t}.$$

Integrating this equation between any two values of t gives

Change in K.E. = Change in W = Work done.

This is one form of the work-energy principle.

Calculation of work done

Since the mathematics necessary for calculating work done directly is not in the course an indirect method has to be used. There are two equivalent methods.
One method is to find the power and integrate it. The other is to use the form of the work-energy principle above and find the change in kinetic energy. The first method can always be applied, the second can only be applied to find the work done by the total force acting on the particle.

Example 6.26

The velocity at time t s of the point of application of the force $(7\mathbf{i} + 6t\mathbf{j} - 8t^2\,\mathbf{k})$ N is $(2t\mathbf{i} + 4\mathbf{j} - 10t^2\ \mathbf{k})\ \mathrm{ms}^{-1}$. Find the work done by the force in the time interval $0 \le t \le 1$.

The power developed by the force is

$$(\,2t \times 7\ + 4 \times 6t\ + (-10t^2\ ) \times (-8t^2\,))\ \mathrm{W} = \ (38t\ + 80t^4\,)\ \mathrm{W}.$$

The work done in the time interval is therefore

$$\int_0^1 (38t + 80t^4)\mathrm{d}t\ \mathrm{J} \ = 35\ \mathrm{J}.$$

Example 6.27

A particle of mass 0.6 kg is moving with a velocity at time t s of $(5t^2\ \mathbf{i}\ + 6t\,\mathbf{j}\ - 7\mathbf{k})\ \mathrm{ms}^{-1}$. Find the work done in the interval $0 \le t\ \le 1$ by the force acting on the particle.

Since the work done by the total force acting on the particle has to be found then this can be done by using the change of kinetic energy.

The kinetic energy is $0.3(25t^4 + 36t^2 + 49)$ J. The change in this from $t = 0$ to $t = 1$ is 18.3 J.

If the work done is found using power, the acceleration and then the force have to be found first. Differentiating the velocity shows that the acceleration is $(10t\mathbf{i} + 6\mathbf{j})$ ms^{-2}, giving the force as $(6t\mathbf{i} + 3.6\mathbf{j})$ N. The power is therefore $(30t^3 + 21.6t)$ J. Integrating this from $t = 0$ to $t = 1$ gives 18.3 J.

Conservation of energy

The idea of potential energy for forces in two and three dimensions is a complicated one and beyond the mathematics you have covered. It is still possible however to define the potential energy due to gravity and that associated with a straight spring.

If the total energy is defined to be kinetic energy + potential energy due to gravity and the force in a spring it is possible to show that

Change in total energy = Work done by all other forces.

Exercises 6.3

1 At time t s the force acting on a particle of mass m kg is $\boldsymbol{F}$ N and at time $t = T$ the particle is moving with velocity $\boldsymbol{v}$ ms^{-1} at the point with position vector $\boldsymbol{R}$ m. Find the position vector of the particle at time t s for

(a) $m = 0.4$, $\boldsymbol{F} = e^{-t}\,\mathbf{i} + 6t^3\,\mathbf{j}$, $T = 0$, $\boldsymbol{v} = 3\mathbf{i} + 5\mathbf{j}$, $\boldsymbol{R} = 2\mathbf{i} + \mathbf{j}$,

(b) $m = 0.2$, $\boldsymbol{F} = 6t\,\mathbf{i} + 12t\,\mathbf{j}$, $T = 1$, $\boldsymbol{v} = 5\mathbf{i} - 6\mathbf{j}$, $\boldsymbol{R} = \mathbf{i} - 7\mathbf{j}$,

(c) $m = 0.5$, $\boldsymbol{F} = \mathbf{i} + 4t\,\mathbf{j} + 8e^{2t}\,\mathbf{k}$, $T = 0$, $\boldsymbol{v} = 3\mathbf{i} - 2\mathbf{j} + 4\mathbf{k}$, $\boldsymbol{R} = 5\mathbf{i} - 4\mathbf{j} + 3\mathbf{k}$,

(d) $m = 1$, $\boldsymbol{F} = 3\mathbf{i} - 6t\,\mathbf{j} + 20t^3\,\mathbf{k}$, $T = 1$, $\boldsymbol{v} = 3\mathbf{i} - 2\mathbf{j} + 4\mathbf{k}$, $\boldsymbol{R} = \mathbf{i} + 6\mathbf{j} - 2\mathbf{k}$.

2 Find the magnitude of the impulse that has to be applied to

(a) a particle of mass 0.2 kg to change its velocity from $(5\mathbf{i} + 6\mathbf{j})$ ms^{-1} to $(9\mathbf{i} + 7\mathbf{j})$ ms^{-1},

(b) a particle of mass 0.3 kg to change its velocity from $(3\mathbf{i} + 4\mathbf{j})$ ms^{-1} to $(5\mathbf{i} + 2\mathbf{j})$ ms^{-1},

(c) a particle of mass 0.4 kg to change its velocity from $(2\mathbf{i} + 4\mathbf{j} + 3\mathbf{k})$ ms^{-1} to $(5\mathbf{i} + 6\mathbf{j} + 8\mathbf{k})$ ms^{-1},

(d) a particle of mass 0.5 kg to change its velocity from $(\mathbf{i} + 8\mathbf{j} + 4\mathbf{k})$ ms^{-1} to $(3\mathbf{i} + 5\mathbf{j} - 3\mathbf{k})$ ms^{-1}.

3 Find the velocity immediately after the impulse is applied of

(a) a particle of mass 0.5 kg moving with a velocity of $(3\mathbf{i} + 8\mathbf{j})$ ms^{-1} immediately before an impulse $(3\mathbf{i} + 8\mathbf{j})$ Ns is applied to it,

(b) a particle of mass 0.25 kg moving with a velocity of $(2\mathbf{i} + 5\mathbf{j} + 3\mathbf{k})$ ms^{-1} immediately before an impulse $(\mathbf{i} + 5\mathbf{j} + 2\mathbf{k})$ Ns is applied to it.

4 A cricket ball of mass 0.15 kg, moving horizontally with speed 15 ms^{-1}, is struck by a batsman so that it moves perpendicular to its original direction with speed 25 ms^{-1}. Find the magnitude and direction of the impulse applied by the batsman.

5 The velocity of a particle of mass m kg at time t s is $\boldsymbol{v}$ ms^{-1}. Find the kinetic energy of the particle for (a) $m = 0.2$, $\boldsymbol{v} = 2t^2\ \mathbf{i} + 7t^4\ \mathbf{j}$,
(b) $m = 0.4$, $\boldsymbol{v} = 6t\ \mathbf{i} + 8t^3\ \mathbf{j}$, (c) $m = 0.8$, $\boldsymbol{v} = 5\cos t\ \mathbf{i} + 3\sin t\ \mathbf{j} + 6t\ \mathbf{k}$,
(d) $m = 1$, $\boldsymbol{v} = 3t\ \mathbf{i} + 4e^{-t}\ \mathbf{j} + 3t\ \mathbf{k}$.

6 The velocity of a particle of mass m kg at time t s is $\boldsymbol{v}$ ms^{-1}. Find the power developed by the force acting on the particle for (a) $m = 0.4$, $\boldsymbol{v} = t^2\ \mathbf{i} + 3t^4\ \mathbf{j}$,
(b) $m = 0.6$, $\boldsymbol{v} = 4t\mathbf{i} + 6t^4\ \mathbf{j}$, (c) $m = 0.6$, $\boldsymbol{v} = 3\cos 2t\ \mathbf{i} - 5\sin 3t\ \mathbf{j} + 6t\ \mathbf{k}$,
(d) $m = 2$, $\boldsymbol{v} = 4t\ \mathbf{i} + 6\,e^{-2t}\ \mathbf{j} + 3t\ \mathbf{k}$.

7 Find (a) the work done by the force in question 5 (a) in the interval $0 \le t \le 1$,
(b) the work done by the force in question 5 (c) in the interval $0 \le t \le \pi$.

Miscellaneous Exercises 6

1 A particle P of mass m kg moves in a plane such that its position vector $\boldsymbol{r}$ m at time t s is given by

$$\boldsymbol{r} = (t^2 - t)\ \mathbf{i} + t\sin \pi t\ \mathbf{j}.$$

Find

(a) the momentum of P when $t = 0$,

(b) the kinetic energy of P when $t = 1$,

(c) the force acting on P when $t = 1$,

(d) the rate of working of the force acting on P when $t = 1$.

2 An ice skater A moves on a flat ice-rink with constant velocity $(10\mathbf{i} + 5\mathbf{j})$ ms^{-1}, passing through the point $(9\mathbf{i} + 8\mathbf{j})$ m at time $t = 0$. A second ice skater B travelling with constant velocity $(p\mathbf{i} + 6\mathbf{j})$ ms^{-1} is at the point $(3\mathbf{i} - \mathbf{j})$ m at time $t = 0$.

(a) If the ice skaters collide find the value of p.

(b) If $p = 11$ show that the ice skaters are closest together when $t = 7.5$ s.

3 A body of mass 2 kg moves so that its position vector at time t s is given by

$$\boldsymbol{r} = (a\sin \pi t + bt^2)\ \mathbf{i} + (c\sin \pi t + dt^2)\ \mathbf{j},$$

where a, b, c and d are constants and distances are measured in metres. Find

(a) the momentum at time t s,

(b) the kinetic energy at time t s (do not simplify),

(c) the force acting on the body at time t s.

At $t = 0$ the speed of the body is 4π ms^{-1}. At $t = \frac{1}{2}$ the body passes through the point $(\mathbf{i} + \mathbf{j})$ m and is travelling in the positive $\mathbf{i}$ direction. Find a, b, c and d. What is the power generated by the force acting on the body at $t = \frac{1}{2}$?

4 A constant force of $(5\mathbf{i} + 3\mathbf{j})$ N is applied to a ring which is on a smooth rod. The rod is fixed in a horizontal plane and joins the origin to the point P of position vector $(3\mathbf{i} + \mathbf{j})$ m. Find the work done in moving the ring from the origin to P.
Given that the ring is of mass 4 kg and that it was initially at rest at the origin, find its speed at P.

5 A particle of mass 3 kg moves in a plane, its position vector at time t s being $\boldsymbol{r}$ m where

$$\boldsymbol{r} = (2\cos t + \sin t)\,\mathbf{i} + (\sin t - 2\cos t)\,\mathbf{j}.$$

Find the values of t
(a) when the speed of the particle is a minimum,
(b) when the force acting on the particle is perpendicular to the velocity vector,
(c) when the power generated by the force is greatest.

6 The velocity $\boldsymbol{v}$ ms^{-1} of a particle of mass 0.4 kg at time t s is given by

$$\boldsymbol{v} = 3\sin 2t\,\mathbf{i} + 5e^{4t}\,\mathbf{j}.$$

Find the force $\boldsymbol{F}$ acting on the particle at time t s. By taking the scalar product of $\boldsymbol{F}$ with an appropriate vector, find the rate of working of this force at time t s.

7 Relative to a fixed origin O, the position vector $\boldsymbol{r}$ m of a particle P at time t s is given by $\boldsymbol{r} = \sin 4t\,\mathbf{i} + \cos 4t\,\mathbf{j} + t^2\,\mathbf{k}$.
(a) Find, in terms of t, the velocity and acceleration of P at time t.
(b) Given also that P is of mass 0.2 kg find, in terms of t, the rate at which the force acting on P is working at time t s.

8 Two points A and B with position vectors $(5\mathbf{i} + 3\mathbf{j} + 14\mathbf{k})$ m and $(11\mathbf{i} + 6\mathbf{j} + 8\mathbf{k})$ m respectively lie on a smooth straight wire. A bead free to move on the wire is acted on by a force $(7\mathbf{i} + 4\mathbf{j} + 3\mathbf{k})$ N.
Find
(a) a unit vector along the wire,
(b) the magnitude of the component of the force parallel to the wire,
(c) the work done by the force in moving the bead from A to B.

9 The velocity of a ball of mass 0.7 kg just before it hits a horizontal floor is $(4\mathbf{i} - 3\mathbf{j})$ ms^{-1} where $\mathbf{i}$ is a horizontal unit vector and $\mathbf{j}$ is a unit vector vertically upwards. Immediately after it leaves the floor the velocity of the ball is $(5\mathbf{i} + 6\mathbf{j})$ ms^{-1}. The time the ball is in contact with the floor may be neglected.
(a) Find the impulse of the floor on the ball in the form $(a\mathbf{i} + b\mathbf{j})$.
(b) Find the change in kinetic energy due to the impact.

10 Three forces $(4\mathbf{i} + 2\mathbf{j} + 6\mathbf{k})$ N, $(2\mathbf{i} - 4\mathbf{j} + 9\mathbf{k})$ N, $(8\mathbf{i} + 5\mathbf{j} - 3\mathbf{k})$ N act at a point P. Find

(a) the resultant $\boldsymbol{R}$ of the forces in the form $a\mathbf{i} + b\mathbf{j} + c\mathbf{k}$,

(b) the magnitude of $\boldsymbol{R}$,

(c) the scalar product of $\boldsymbol{R}$ with the vector $\mathbf{i} + 3\mathbf{j} + 4\mathbf{k}$,

(d) the cosine of the angle between $\boldsymbol{R}$ and the vector $\mathbf{i} + 3\mathbf{j} + 4\mathbf{k}$,

(e) the total work done by the forces acting on P as it moves from the point with position vector $(2\mathbf{i} + 4\mathbf{j} + 7\mathbf{k})$ m to the point with position vector $(5\mathbf{i} + 3\mathbf{j} + 11\mathbf{k})$ m.

11 The velocity $\boldsymbol{v}$ ms^{-1} of a particle P at time t s is given by $\boldsymbol{v} = t\,\mathbf{i} + \sin t\,\mathbf{j}$.

(a) Find the acceleration of P at time t s.

(b) Given that the particle has position vector $(4\mathbf{i} + 3\mathbf{j})$ m when $t = 0$, find the position vector of P at time t s.

12 At time t s the position vector $\mathbf{r}$ m, of a moving particle P, is given by

$$\mathbf{r} = (2t - 1)\mathbf{i} + 4\cos 3t\,\mathbf{j} + 4\sin 3t\,\mathbf{k}.$$

Find

(a) the velocity $\boldsymbol{v}$ ms^{-1} of P at time t seconds,

(b) the time when $\boldsymbol{v}$ and $\boldsymbol{r}$ are perpendicular.

13 At time t hours the position vectors, in units of 100 km, relative to a fixed origin, of two aircraft A and B are, respectively,

$$2\mathbf{i} + 4\mathbf{j} + 7\mathbf{k} + t(4\mathbf{i} + 3\mathbf{j} + 4\mathbf{k}) \text{ and } 13\mathbf{i} + 3\mathbf{j} + 7\mathbf{k} + t(2\mathbf{i} + 2\mathbf{j} + \mathbf{k}).$$

(a) Explain why you can say that both aircrafts are moving with constant velocities.

(b) Find the speed of aircraft B, stating its units.

(c) Find, in terms of t, an expression for AB^2 at time t hours and hence determine the time at which the aircraft are closest together.

14 Two particles P and Q move with constant velocities $(5\mathbf{i} + k\mathbf{j})$ ms^{-1} and $(4\mathbf{i} + 3\mathbf{j})$ ms^{-1} respectively, where k is a constant. At time $t = 0$ the position vectors, in metres, of P and Q are $4\mathbf{i} + 2\mathbf{j}$ and $7\mathbf{i} + 14\mathbf{j}$ respectively. Find the position vector of Q relative to P at time t s.

(a) Find the value of k such that P and Q collide and the value of t when this collision would occur.

(b) In the particular case when $k = 4$ show that

$$PQ^2 = 2t^2 - 30t + 153$$

and find the value of t when P and Q are closest together and their distance apart at this time.

Find also the length of time for which the distance between P and Q is less than or equal to 9 m.

15 A particle of mass 0.2 kg moves on a smooth horizontal plane. Its position vector $\boldsymbol{r}$, in metres, at time t s is given by

$$\boldsymbol{r} = 4t^3\ \mathbf{i} + 4t^4\ \mathbf{j}.$$

Find

(a) the kinetic energy when $t = 0.5$,

(b) the cosine of the angle between the velocity when $t = 0.5$ and the vector $4\mathbf{i} - 3\mathbf{j}$.

16 When an impulse is applied to a particle of mass 0.3 kg moving with constant velocity $(11\mathbf{i} + 7\mathbf{j})$ ms^{-1} on a smooth horizontal table, its velocity is changed to $(10\mathbf{i} + 14\mathbf{j})$ ms^{-1}. Find

(a) the impulse,

(b) the change in the kinetic energy of the particle.

17 Relative to a fixed origin, the position vector, $\boldsymbol{r}$, of a particle P is given by

$$\boldsymbol{r} = 3 \sin t\ \mathbf{i} + 5 \cos t\ \mathbf{j},$$

where $\boldsymbol{r}$ is measured in metres and t denotes the time in seconds.

(a) Find the velocity of P at time t s and show that its speed is v ms^{-1} where

$$v^2 = 17 - 8 \cos 2t.$$

Hence find the maximum and minimum values of v.

(b) Find the cosine of the angle between the velocity and acceleration of P when $t = \dfrac{\pi}{4}$.

(c) Given that the particle is of mass 0.3 kg, find the rate of working at time t s of the force acting on P and the maximum rate of working of this force.

18 The position vector in metres at time t seconds, relative to a fixed origin O, of a particle P moving in a horizontal plane is given by

$$\boldsymbol{r} = \frac{2}{\pi}(\cos \pi t\ \mathbf{i} + \sin \pi t\ \mathbf{j}).$$

Given that P is of mass 0.2 kg, find the horizontal force acting on it at time t seconds.

When $t = 0$ a second particle Q moving with constant velocity $(-6\mathbf{i} + 8\mathbf{j})$ ms^{-1} is at the point with position vector $\boldsymbol{b}$, metres. Find the position vector of Q at any time in terms of $\boldsymbol{b}$, $\mathbf{i}$, $\mathbf{j}$ and t. Determine $\boldsymbol{b}$ given that the particles collide when $t = \dfrac{1}{2}$.

19 At noon a ship A passes through the origin O and is moving with constant speed u kmh^{-1} in the direction of the vector $3\mathbf{i} + 4\mathbf{j}$. At the same time a second ship B, moving with constant speed 10 kmh^{-1} in the direction of $\mathbf{i}$, is at the point with position vector $10(-\mathbf{i} + \mathbf{j})$ km.

(a) Find the position vectors of the ships at time t hours after noon.

(b) Find u such that the ships are on a collision course and the time at which collision would take place.

(c) Assuming that $u = 10$

(i) show that at time t hours after noon $AB^2 = 80t^2 - 240t + 200$,

(ii) find the time at which the two ships are closest together,

(iii) find the time when AB is perpendicular to the direction of the velocity of ship A.

20 At noon the position vectors, relative to a fixed origin, of two aircraft A and B are $(30\mathbf{i} + 20\mathbf{j} + 10\mathbf{k})$ km and $(-10\mathbf{i} + 15\mathbf{k})$ km respectively. Aircraft A is moving with constant velocity $(-40\mathbf{i} + p\mathbf{j})$ kmh^{-1} and aircraft B is moving with constant velocity $(120\mathbf{i} + 200\mathbf{j} + q\mathbf{k})$ kmh^{-1} where p and q are constants.

(a) Write down the position vectors of the two aircraft at time t hours after noon.

(b) Show that the vector representing the line AB is given by

$$((-40 + 160t)\mathbf{i} + (-20 + (200 - p)t)\mathbf{j} + (5 + qt)\mathbf{k}) \text{ km.}$$

(c) Find the values of p and q such that the aircraft collide.

Chapter 7

First Order Differential Equations

After working through this chapter you should be able

- to recognise the different types of differential equations,
- to solve first order differential equations with variables separable
- to model simple "real life" problems as differential equations and solve the resulting equations.

7.1 Basic definitions and notations

Simple examples of differential equations are

(a) $\dfrac{dx}{dt} = t$, (b) $\dfrac{dy}{dx} = xy$, (c) $\dfrac{dy}{dx} = ye^x$, (d) $\dfrac{d^2x}{dt^2} = x$

(d) $\dfrac{dt}{dx} = \sqrt{xy}$, (f) $\dfrac{dr}{d\theta} = \cos\theta$, (g) $\dfrac{d^2x}{dt^2} + 5\dfrac{dx}{dt} + 6x = t$, (h) $\dfrac{dv}{dt} + v = t$

A differential equation is a relation between the derivatives of one variable (e.g. x) with respect to another variable (e.g. t) and given functions of the two variables. The variable being differentiated is called the **'dependent variable'** and the other variable is called the **'independent variable'**. In (a), (d) and (g) above, the dependent variable is x and the independent variable t. In (b), (c) and (e) above, the dependent variable is y and the independent variable x. In (f) above, the dependent variable is r and the independent variable θ whilst in (h) the dependent variable is v and the independent variable t. Any pairs of letters can be used for the dependent and independent variables and you need to be very careful in answering questions to use the same variables as given in the question. In most of the worked examples the dependent variable will be x and the independent variable t but other combinations will be used in the exercises.

Order of a differential equation

The order of a differential equation is the order of the highest derivative occurring in it. The equations in examples (a), (b), (c), (e), (f) and (h) are all first order whereas those in examples (d) and (g) are second order.

Basic facts

In order to obtain a unique (i.e. the only one) solution you need to specify more than just the equation. For the example in (a) i.e.

$$\frac{dx}{dt} = t,$$

integrating the left hand side with respect to t gives x and integrating the right hand side with respect to t gives $\frac{1}{2}t^2$ together with an arbitrary constant, A say. Therefore

$$x = \frac{1}{2}t^2 + A,$$

this means that for each value of A there will be a different function satisfying the differential equation and therefore there will be an infinite number of different solutions of the differential equation. However if x is given for one value of t, then A can be found and then a unique solution found for x. For example if $x = 3$ for $t = 2$ then $A = 1$ and $x = \frac{1}{2}t^2 + 1$.

It is true in general that :-

(a) a unique solution of a first order differential equation can be found if the value of the dependent variable is known for one value of the independent variable. This means that in example (c) above, a unique solution can be found for y if its value is given (e.g. y = 2) for a given value of x (e.g. $x = 3$).

(b) a unique solution of a second order differential equation can be found if the value of the dependent variable and the first derivative is known for one value of the independent variable. This means that in example (d) above, a unique solution can be found for x if its value is given (e.g. $x = 3$), and the value of $\frac{dx}{dt}$ (e.g. $\frac{dx}{dt} = 4$) for a given value of t (e.g. $t = 0$).

General solution

The general solution of a first (second) order equation is one such that from it you can obtain the unique solution with the value of the dependent variable (and, for second order equations, its first derivative) given for one value of the independent variable. In practice this means that the general solution of a first order equation will, as in example (a) above, involve an arbitrary constant. The general solution of a second order equation will involve two arbitrary constants.

The general method of solving differential equations is to find the general solution and then fit the constants to satisfy any given conditions.

7.2 First order equations, variables separable

You will cover these equations in P3 but in case you have not come to that part of the course yet the basic ideas will be summarised here. Equations of this type often occur in Mechanics, particularly in problems involving resisted motion. The technique will be first illustrated with some simple examples.

Example 7.1

Find the general solution of

$$\frac{dx}{dt} = x^2$$

and the unique solution such that $x = 1$ for $t = 3$.

The left hand side can be integrated with respect to t to give x but this will not work on the right hand side since x is an unknown function of t and there is no way of integrating it. The equation can however be rearranged so that all the "x" dependence is on the same side of the equation as the derivative and all the "t" dependence is on the other side. This gives

$$\frac{1}{x^2}\frac{dx}{dt} = 1,$$

this equation can now be integrated with respect to t i.e.

$$\int\frac{dx}{x^2} = \int dt.$$

The left hand side of this can be integrated with respect to x and the right hand side integrated with respect to t giving

$$-\frac{1}{x} = t + c,$$

where c is an arbitrary constant. This is the general solution of the equation. Substituting $x = 1$ and $t = 3$ gives $c = -4$ so that

$$-\frac{1}{x} = t - 4$$

is the unique solution with the value 1 for $t = 3$.

The equation can be rearranged to give

$$x = \frac{1}{4 - t}.$$

If this is substituted back into the original differential equation then you can check that it is satisfied as is the condition for $t = 3$. Differential equations are one of the few topics where it is possible to check fairly easily that you have got the correct answer and it is always worth carrying out the check.

In problems like this, where x is given for a value of t, it is possible to avoid introducing an arbitrary constant by integrating between limits. In this case the limits for x would be between 1 and x and that for t between 3 and t. So that

$$\int_1^x \frac{dx}{x^2} = \int_3^t dt .$$

This becomes on evaluating the integrals

$$1 - \frac{1}{x} = t - 3,$$

which is equivalent to the result obtained above.

Example 7.2

Find the solution of the differential equation

$$\frac{dx}{dt} = 2e^{t-x}$$

with $x = 0$ for $t = \ln 2$.

Again the right hand side cannot be integrated directly with respect to t since x is unknown. It is however again possible to rearrange the equation so that all the "x" dependence is on the same side of the equation as the derivative and all the "t" dependence is on the other side. Carrying out this rearrangement gives

$$e^x \frac{dx}{dt} = 2e^t,$$

integrating with respect to t gives

$$\int e^x\, dx = 2 \int e^t\, dt.$$

Evaluating the integral shows that

$$e^x - 1 = 2(e^t - 2),$$

$$e^x = 2e^t - 3,$$

i.e.

taking logarithms of both sides gives

$$x = \ln\left(2e^t - 3\right)$$

You can again verify that this solution satisfies the differential equation and the condition when $t = \ln 2$.

Example 7.3

Find the solution v of the differential equation

$$\frac{dv}{dt} - v = 4$$

with $v = 4$ when $t = 0$.

This equation can be rearranged so that the "v" dependence is on the same side of the equation as the derivative and any "t" dependence is on the other. This means that the

v has first to be moved to the right hand side of the equation and then both sides divided by $v + 4$, i.e.
$$\frac{1}{v+4}\frac{\mathrm{d}v}{\mathrm{d}t} = 4$$

Both sides can now be integrated with respect to t so that
$$\int \frac{\mathrm{d}v}{v+4} = 4\int \mathrm{d}t\,,$$

In order to satisfy the condition at $t = 0$ the left hand side has to be integrated from 4 to v and the right hand side from 0 to t giving
$$\int_4^v \frac{\mathrm{d}v}{v+4} = 4\int_0^t \mathrm{d}t\,,$$

i.e.
$$\ln\frac{v+4}{8} = 4t\,.$$

Taking the exponential of both sides gives
$$v = 8\mathrm{e}^{4t} - 4\,.$$

General method

The method used above of rearranging the equation is known as the method of separation of variables and works for equations of the type
$$\frac{\mathrm{d}x}{\mathrm{d}t} = \mathrm{f}(x)\,\mathrm{g}(t) \text{ or, equivalently, } \frac{\mathrm{d}y}{\mathrm{d}x} = \mathrm{f}(x)\,\mathrm{g}(y)$$

where f and g are given functions. Sometimes the equation has to be rearranged, as in Example 7.3, to get it into the correct form.

The steps in the solution are

(i) rearrange so that terms involving the dependent variable are on the same side of the equation as the derivative and the terms depending on the independent variable are on the other side e.g.
$$\frac{1}{\mathrm{f}(x)}\frac{\mathrm{d}x}{\mathrm{d}t} = \mathrm{g}(t),$$

(ii) integrate both sides of the equation with respect to the independent variable e.g.
$$\int \frac{1}{\mathrm{f}(x)}\mathrm{d}x = \int \mathrm{g}\,(t)\;\mathrm{d}t,$$

if conditions are given for one set of values of the variables use these in the limits of integration,

(iii) invert to obtain the dependent variable in terms of the independent variable. You may not always be able to do this and may only be able to obtain a general relation between the variables.

Exercises 7.1

Find the general solutions of the following differential equations.

1 $\dfrac{dx}{dt} = \dfrac{x}{t}$.

2 $\dfrac{dx}{dt} = x^3$.

3 $\dfrac{dv}{dt} = -\dfrac{1}{v^2}$.

4 $\dfrac{dr}{d\theta} = r \tan \theta$

Find the solutions of the following differential equations satisfying the conditions stated.

5 $\dfrac{dx}{dt} = x,\ x = 4$ for $t = 0$.

6 $\dfrac{dx}{dt} = -\dfrac{1}{x},\ x = 5$ for $t = 1$.

7 $\dfrac{dx}{dt} = t^3 x^2,\ x = 1$ for $t = 1$.

8 $\dfrac{dy}{dx} = e^x + y = 0$ for $x = 0$.

9 $\dfrac{dv}{dt} + 3v = 4,\ v = 1$ for $t = 0$.

10 $\dfrac{dv}{dt} + 3v = 4,\ v = 5$ for $t = 0$.

11 $(xy + 2y)\dfrac{dy}{dx} = y^2 - 1,\ y = \sqrt{10}$ for $x = 1$.

7.3 Modelling involving differential equations

In your course, and in examinations, you may be required to find the differential equations to model a problem in an area in which you have no previous knowledge (e.g. population growth, radioactive decay). This is not as difficult as it sounds since the problems will always be stated in a form where sufficient information will be given to translate it into one of solving a differential equation, without knowing any additional background detail. We start off by looking at problems not involving Mechanics since you already know the basic mechanical principles and have already some practice of modelling mechanical problems as simple differential equations . You will also meet modelling of mechanical problems as differential equations in M3 and, very briefly, at the end of this section.

Modelling other than in Mechanics

One of the first things to determine when setting up a model is what is the unknown (i.e. the dependent variable). In examination questions, this is usually made clear. It is also necessary to pick the independent variable, this is usually obvious and is very often the time. For example, you may be told that the number in a population varies with time in a particular way. This tells you immediately that the number in the population should be the dependent variable and the independent variable should be the time. You need to look for certain key words which will help you to "translate" the problem into one involving a differential equation. The most common phrase which tells you what to do is "rate of change" and similar phrases given below. Many problems reduce to the solution of a first order differential equation and we start off by looking at typical problems of this type.

Problems involving rates of change and leading to first order equations

Most problems which can be modelled as differential equations involve some information about the rate of change of a variable x (say) normally with time t, ie. information about $\frac{\mathrm{d}x}{\mathrm{d}t}$. Other phrases which imply rate of change are rate of growth or of decay. Very often the information is given in a way which also suggests the appropriate choice of both dependent and independent variables. For example, you may be told that the amount of money in a bank account grows with time in a particular way. This tells you that the dependent variable should be the amount in the account and the independent variable should be the time.

The simplest type of situation that may occur is that the rate of change of a quantity, for example, the number in a population, is given explicitly either as a constant c or as a function f(t) of time. The given data suggests, in this case, taking the dependent variable to be the number in the population at time t. If this is denoted by x then the rate of change of x is $\frac{\mathrm{d}x}{\mathrm{d}t}$ and the information can be rewritten as

$$\frac{\mathrm{d}x}{\mathrm{d}t} = c \quad \text{or} \quad \frac{\mathrm{d}x}{\mathrm{d}t} = f(t),$$

and the initial problem has now been transformed into one of solving a fairly simple differential equation.

In most cases all that will be known about the rate of change of x is that it will depend in some way on x. For example, it may be known to be proportional to x^n, where n is a known constant (often an integer). The phrase proportional (or directly proportional) to a variable means equal to some constant times the variable and very often modelling questions require introducing a constant of proportionality. The above information therefore translates into the differential equation

$$\frac{\mathrm{d}x}{\mathrm{d}t} = kx^n,$$

where k is a constant.

If the rate of change had been stated to be inversely proportional to x^n, then this would mean that it was equal to $\frac{k}{x^n}$ so that n would be replaced by $-n$ in the differential equation.

In many cases, the constant k may not be given explicitly but values of x will be given for two values of t and these values can be used to find k, and you may be asked to predict the value of x at some subsequent time.

Example 7.4

The rate of growth of the population of the United States at the beginning of the last century is assumed to be directly proportional to the number in the population. The population figures, in millions, for 1810 and 1820 are 7.2 and 9. Estimate the population in 1840.

In this case, the unknown is the number in the population, this will be denoted by x. The independent variable is the time t in years and to simplify the algebra $t = 0$ is taken to be 1810.

The assumption is that $\frac{\mathrm{d}x}{\mathrm{d}t} = kx$

where k is a constant.

Separating the variables and integrating

$$\int \frac{\mathrm{d}x}{x} = k\int dt$$

$$\ln x = kt + c.$$

Since $x = 7.2$ for $t = 0$, it follows that $c = \ln 7.2$

and $$x = 7.2\mathrm{e}^{kt}$$

The population for t = 10 is given as 9 and this gives an equation to determine t namely

$$9 = 7.2e^{k10},$$

solving this gives k = 0.022, so that the population in 1840 is predicted to be 13.93 million. One important thing to notice about the solution is that it predicts infinite growth, this is unrealistic and not consistent with observation. This means that a more satisfactory model has to be found which does not predict infinite growth.

A model which does this is one based on the differential equation

$$\frac{dx}{dt} = kx(n - x),$$

an equation of this type is solved in Example 7.7 (see also question 1, Miscellaneous Exercises 7).

Example 7.5

The volume of a raindrop decreases, due to evaporation, at a rate of k times its surface area. Given that its volume is V_0 at time t = 0 find its volume at any subsequent time t.

In this question, the dependent variable is the volume V of the sphere and the first step is to express the surface area in terms of the volume. If the radius is r, then the volume is $\frac{4\pi}{3}r^3$ and the surface area is $4\pi r^2$. Substituting for r in terms of V gives the surface areas as $cV^{\frac{2}{3}}$ where c = $cV^{\frac{2}{3}}(4\pi)^{\frac{1}{3}}$. Therefore

$$\frac{dV}{dt} = -kcV^{\frac{2}{3}},$$

the minus arises since the volume decreases. The variables may be separated giving

$$\frac{dV}{V^{\frac{2}{3}}} = -kc\,dt,$$

integrating gives $\quad 3V^{\frac{1}{3}} = -kct + A,$

where A is a constant. The condition $V = V_0$ at $t = 0$ shows that $A = 3V_0^{\frac{1}{3}}$ and

therefore $\quad V = \left[V_0^{\frac{1}{3}} - \frac{kct}{3}\right]^3$

Example 7.6

Newton's law of cooling states that when the temperature of a body is above the temperature of its surroundings, then it decreases at a rate directly proportional to the difference between its temperature and the surrounding temperature.
A body at a temperature of 190°C is immersed in liquid which is maintained at a constant temperature of 50°C. In one minute, the temperature of the body decreases to 120°C, find how long it takes for the temperature to drop to 85°C.

If T° denotes the temperature of the body, then Newton's law gives

$$\frac{\mathrm{d}T}{\mathrm{d}t} = -k(T-50),$$

where T is the time measured in minutes and introducing the minus sign means that the constant k is positive.
Separating the variables and integrating gives

$$\int \frac{\mathrm{d}T}{(T-50)} = -k\int dt$$

and therefore

$$\ln\,(T-50) = -kt + C$$

Substituting $T = 190$ when $t = 0$ gives $C = \ln 140$. Substituting $T = 120$ when $t = 1$ gives $k = \ln 2$, so that

$$t\ln 2 = \ln\left(\frac{140}{T-50}\right)$$

The time taken to reach a temperature of 85°C satisfies the equation

$$t\ln 2 \;=\; \ln 4 \;=\; 2\ln 2$$

giving $t = 2$.

Example 7.7

In a simple model of an epidemic it is assumed that the population may be divided into those that are infected and those susceptible. (This assumes no deaths or recovery). It is further assumed that the rate of spread of the disease is k times the product of the number susceptible and the number infected. At time $t = 0$, one person is infected and there are $n+1$ people in the population. Find the number infected at time t later.

If the number infected is denoted by x, then the number susceptible is $n+1-x$ and therefore, since the number infected is increasing,

$$\frac{\mathrm{d}x}{\mathrm{d}t} = kx(n+1-x)$$

This equation is of the type in which the variables can be separated and

$$\int \frac{\mathrm{d}x}{x(n+1-x)} = k\int dt\,,$$

using partial fractions show that the equations can be rewritten as

$$\frac{1}{n+1}\int\left(\frac{\mathrm{d}x}{x} + \frac{\mathrm{d}x}{n+1-x}\right) = k\int \mathrm{d}t$$

Integrating the equation gives

$$\ln\frac{x}{n+1-x} = k(n+1)\,t + c\,,$$

where c is a constant. The condition $x = 1$ at $t = 0$ gives $c = -\ln(n)$ and therefore

$$k(n+1)\,t = \ln\frac{nx}{n+1-x}.$$

Taking the exponential of both sides of this equation and rearranging the resulting equation gives $x = \dfrac{(n+1)e^{k(n+1)t}}{n+e^{k(n+1)t}}$,

as t becomes infinite this tends to $n+1$ showing that eventually the whole population becomes infected.

Example 7.8

In a particular chemical process in order to produce one unit of a chemical X, 2 units of a chemical A are used and 3 units of a chemical B are used. Initially, there are 10 units of A and 8 units of B present. The rate of production of X is directly proportional to the product of the amounts of A and B remaining. Find the form of the differential equation satisfied by x, the quantity of X produced by time t.

To produce x units, $2x$ units of A and $3x$ units of B will have been used. Therefore the amounts remaining of these substances are $10-2x$ units and $8-3x$ units respectively. Therefore the required differential equation is

$$\frac{\mathrm{d}x}{\mathrm{d}t} = k(10-2x)(8-3x),$$

where k is a constant.

Nett rate of change

In many practical circumstances there may be several sources for the rate of change of a quantity and these changes have to be assembled together to arrive at a total (or nett) rate of change. A simple example is that of population growth where both births and deaths affect the growth rate and normally the birth and death rates are known. If the birth and death rates are both assumed to be directly proportional to the number x in the population, then the contribution of births to the growth rate is of the form px and the contribution of the deaths is of the form $-qx$ (taking both p and q to be positive so that the minus indicates a decrease). The nett rate is therefore $(p-q)x$ and therefore

$$\frac{dx}{dt} = (p-q)x\,.$$

There are many problems of the above type where input (e.g. birth) and output (.e.g death) rates are given or there are two causes of a growth rate, for example in a population there could be birth and death rates and also terms arising from emigration and immigration. In these circumstances, the nett rate of change has to be found from the equation.

$$\text{Nett rate of change} = \text{rate of input} - \text{rate of output}$$

<u>**Example 7.9**</u>

The growth rate of a colony of bacteria, in units per day, is $\frac{1}{4}$ of the number of bacteria present at any time. The bacteria are extracted from the colony at the constant rate of R units per day. At time $t = 0$, the number in the colony is N, find the number present at time t days later.

If x denotes the number of bacteria at time t days, then the "input" per day is $\frac{1}{4}x$ and the output per day is R. Therefore

$$\frac{dx}{dt} = \frac{1}{4}x - R.$$

Separating the variables and integrating gives

$$4\int \frac{dx}{x-4R} = \int dt$$

and so $$x - 4R = ae^{\frac{t}{4}}.$$

At $t = 0$ $x = N$ and therefore $$a = N - 4R, \text{ so that}$$

$$x = (N - 4R)e^{\frac{t}{4}} + 4R\,.$$

Exercises 7.2

1 The growth rate of a colony of bacteria is directly proportional to the number in the population. The number of bacteria grew from 100 to 400 in 24 hours. Find the number of bacteria after 12 hours.

2 In a model of the response of the ear to a stimulus, it is assumed that the rate of change of response with respect to the stimulus is inversely proportional to the stimulus. Find the general form of the response in terms of the stimulus.

3 The amount of radium in a piece of lead decreases at a rate directly proportional to the amount present. In 1500 years the amount of radium decreases to one half its original value. Find the fraction remaining after 2500 years.

4 The death and birth rates in an ant colony are both directly proportional to the number in the colony. The death rate is such that, if there were no births, the population would reduce to one half its value in 1 week. However in actual fact, the population doubles in 2 weeks. Find the birth rate.

5 The population of a city is assumed to increase at a rate directly proportional to the number in the population and the growth rate is such that an initial population of 40,000 increases to 80,000 in 50 years. Immigration, which is assumed to occur at a uniform rate, accounts for a uniform rate of increase of 400 people per year. Find the population after 10 years.

6 In a model used by insurance companies it is assumed that money deposited grows at a constant rate per year equal to 0.06 times the amount in an account at any given instant. Determine the amount in an account 3 years after £500 has been deposited.

7 A body at a temperature of 100°C is placed in a medium kept at a constant temperature of 20°C. After 10 minutes, the temperature of the body is 60°C, find its temperature after 40 minutes.

8 One unit of a new substance X is formed by combining one unit of A with one unit of B. Initially, there are 10 units of A and 8 units of B. The rate of formation of X is directly proportional to the product of the amounts of A and B remaining. One unit of X is formed in 5 minutes. Determine the number of units formed in 10 minutes.

9 In a model of population growth of protozoa, it is assumed that the population grows at a rate at any time equal to twice the number in the population at that time. As well as the growth factor, competition between the protozoa will produce a decrease in the rate of growth equal 0.01 times the square of the number present. Formulate the differential equation satisfied by the number in the population and find the number in the population at time t given that there are 5 at time $t = 0$.

Miscellaneous Exercises 7

1 The number in a population at time t is denoted by x. In a particular model, the variable x satisfies the differential equation

$$\left(\frac{1}{x}+\frac{1}{n-x}\right)\frac{dx}{dt}=k$$

where k is a constant. At time $t = 0$, the population has $\frac{1}{4}n$ individuals. Assuming that x never reaches the value n, show that at time t

$$\frac{3x}{n-x}=e^{kt}.$$

Given that the population has $\frac{1}{2}n$ individuals at time T, find the number in the population at time $2T$.

2 In a particular model of a bank account, the amount in the account at time t years is denoted by £x, where both x and t are assumed to vary continuously. It is assumed that, at any time, there is a continuous inflow of money (due to interest) at a rate per year equal to θ times the amount in the account at that time; θ is known as the force of interest and may vary with t. There is also a continuous flow of money out of the account at a constant rate of £r per year. Explain why x satisfies the differential equation

$$\frac{dx}{dt}=\theta x - r.$$

(a) Find the general solutions of this equation for $\theta = 0.1$and $r = 100$, and find the particular solutions such that

(i) $x = 900$ when $t = 0$

(ii) $x = 1100$ when $t = 0$.

Sketch the graph of x against t in both cases.

(b) In a particular model when $r = 0$, the forces of interest is $a + bt$, where a and b are constants and, at time $t = 0$, $x = 10000$. Find x at any subsequent time t and given that $x = 16000$ at time $t = 2$, find θ when $t = 1$.

3 Find the particular solution of the differential equation

$$\frac{dy}{dx} = \left(y^2+1\right)\left(x^4+.1\right)$$

such that $y = 1$ for $x = 5$.

4 Translate into words the law of cooling expressed by the differential equation

$$\frac{dT}{dx} = \lambda(T-A)$$

where t is the time, T the temperature of a hot body, A is the temperature of its surroundings and λ is a positive constant.

If A is constant, show that

$$T_0 - T = (T_0 - A)(1 - e^{-\lambda t})$$

where T_0 is the value of the temperature of the body at time $t = 0$. If the body, starting at time $t = 0$, cools from 80 ºC to 60 ºC in 15 minutes, and from 60 ºC to 50 ºC in a further 15 minutes, find λ.

5 It is known from experiments that water escapes from a flat-bottomed tank through an orifice in its base at a rate of approximately $2.66A\sqrt{h}\ \mathrm{m^3s^{-1}}$, where A is the orifice area in square metres and h is the height in metres of the water surface above the orifice.

A tank 1 m deep has a rectangular cross-section of 2m by 3m. The tank is initially filled with water. At time $t = 0$, the water starts to escape through a circular orifice in the base of the tank, the orifice being of radius 0.01m. Taking π to be 3.14 and calculating correct to two significant figures, show that at time t s

$$\frac{\mathrm{d}h}{\mathrm{d}t} = -0.00014\sqrt{h}$$

How long does the tank take to empty?

6 The spread of a non-fatal disease through a large population of M people can be studied theoretically as follows. The rate at which people who are currently healthy are being infected is 0.01 times the product of the number that are healthy and the proportion P of the total population that are infected. The rate of recovery of infected people is 0.009 times the number of people that are infected. Noting that the number of people that are infected at time t is MP, show that the process can be approximated by the differential equation

$$\frac{\mathrm{d}P}{\mathrm{d}t} = 0.001(1 - 10P)P,$$

explaining any necessary assumptions.

Find P in terms of t, given that $P = 0.01$ when $t = 0$. Estimate the population infected when t is very large.

7 An economic theory suggests that the relationship between the national debt £D and the national income £I can be represented by the following differential equations:

$$\frac{\mathrm{d}D}{\mathrm{d}t} = aI, \qquad \frac{\mathrm{d}I}{\mathrm{d}t} = bI,$$

where a and b are positive constants. If I_0 and D_0 are the initial values of I and D, respectively, show that

$$D = \frac{aI_0}{b}\left(e^{bt} - 1\right) + D_0.$$

ANSWERS

Exercises 1.1

1. $84t^2 + 12t$
2. $9t^2 + 8t$
3. $2t^4 + 3t^3 + t^2 + 2t$
4. $t^5 + t^4 - 3t + 1$
5. $1 + 5t + e^{-t}$
6. 2, 9
7. $5t^3 + t + 2$

Exercises 1.2

1. 4 ms^{-1}
2. 9 ms^{-1}
3. 40.24 ms^{-1}, 2.48m
4. (i) 6.24 ms^{-1} (ii) $6.12t - 1.5t^2$ (iii) 14.04

Miscellaneous Exercises 1

1. (a) 2m (b) 14 ms^{-2}
2. $\frac{32}{27}$, 2, $\frac{4}{3}$ ms^{-1}
3. $4 \ln \frac{4}{3}$
5. $2 < t < 5$, 8.4
6. $p = 4,\ q = -\frac{8}{3},\ r = \frac{4}{9},\ a = 4,\ b = -\frac{4}{3}$, distance = 4 m
7. $\frac{128}{3}$ m, $-0.4t$ N
8. (a) 5 ms^{-1}, 20 ms^{-1} (b) 2 m, 9 m, 11 m
9. $\left(\frac{P-R}{M}\right)\frac{T}{2}$, $\left(\frac{P-R}{M}\right)\frac{T^2}{3}$, $\frac{3(P^2-R^2)}{16M}T$, $\frac{R(P-R)}{2M}T$
10. 13.3 kW

Exercises 2.1

1. 1.6 J
2. 1.86 m
3. 245 J
4. 11.76 J
5. 3.02 J
6. 26.1 N

7. (i) 804.4 J (ii) 1326 J (a) 177.5 N (b) 251 N
9. 69 kJ
10. 9.125 N

Exercises 2.2

1. (i) 6 J (ii) –14 J
2. (i) 22 J (ii) 5.5 J (iii) 1 J

Exercises 2.3

1. 1 J
2. 8 J
3. 39.1 J
4. 9 J
5. 33 J
6. 0.15 J, 2.25 J
7. 0.25 J

Exercises 2.4

1. (i) 6.4 J (ii) 193.6 kJ (iii) 440 J
2. 67.5 kJ
3. 18.7 ms^{-1}
4. (i) 2 kN (ii) $80000x$ where x m is distance entered
5. 68400 J
6. (i) 1132 J (ii) 1.5 ms^{-1}
7. 9.9 ms^{-1}
8. 73.2 J, 2.05 ms^{-1}
9. 2.36 J, 8.74 ms^{-1}
10. (i) 2.48 J (ii) 0.28
11. 13.2 m
12. 9.22 ms^{-1}
13. $u > 6.32$

Exercises 2.5

1. 4.41 J, 20.8 kJ, 98 J
2. –20.58 kJ
3. 14 ms^{-1}
4. 1.98 m
5. 1.60 m
6. $\sqrt{3gh/2}$

7. $0.75\ ms^{-1}$
8. $10\ ms^{-1}$
9. $.85\left(ga\right)^{\frac{1}{2}}$
10. 2.73 m
11. 3 m
12. 1.73 m
13. 3 m
14. 1.805 m

Exercises 2.6

1. 24 exp $(6t)$
2. (i) 30 kJ (ii) 11.04 kJ
3. $50.8\ ms^{-1}$
4. (i) 72.3 kW (ii) 96.4 kW
5. 4.71 kW

Exercises 2.7

1. 9 kW
2. 9 kW
3. 500 N
4. $8\ ms^{-1}$
5. $0.2\ ms^{-1}$
6. 12.5 kW, $9.3\ ms^{-1}$
7. 48 kN, 480 kW, $20\ ms^{-1}$
8. $20.5\ ms^{-1}$, 0.24
9. $32.1\ ms^{-1}$, $0.96\ ms^{-2}$
10. 50 kW, $0.02\ ms^{-2}$, 0.036
11. 18.24 kW, 0.1
12. $0.75\ ms^{-2}$
13. $20\ ms^{-1}$

Miscellaneous Exercises 2

1. (a) 1.28 m (b) $8.01\ ms^{-1}$
2. (b) 5.1 m (c) 1.18 J
3. 540 N, 27 N
4. (a) 59150 J (b) 172323, 93.3 N
5. 64 kJ, 29.4 J, 126.6 kJ
6. 15 J

7. $\frac{mgR}{6}$, $\frac{\sqrt{gR}}{6}$
8. $8\ ms^{-1}$
9. 313.6 N, 0.245 m
10. (i) $3.16\ ms^{-1}$ (ii) $2.9\ ms^{-1}$
11. $-3.19\ ms^{-2}$, $3.078\ ms^{-1}$
12. $2a$
14. $4.5l$
15. $\sqrt{2gx}$
16. $\sqrt{\frac{18ga}{5}}$
17. (i) $\frac{7a}{9}$ below 0 (ii) $\frac{2}{3}(ag)^{\frac{1}{2}}$
18. 40500 J, 7840 J, 48.34 kW
19. $\frac{P}{20}$, 14000, $0.6\ ms^{-2}$
20. $100\ (700 + R)$, 300
21. $\frac{1000R}{V} - Mg\sin\alpha - Ma$ newtons
22. (i) $20\ ms^{-1}$ (ii) $0.75\ ms^{-2}$
23. 38 kW (i) $0.475\ ms^{-2}$ (iii) 1382.5 N, No, $m \leq 2000$
24. 20 kW, $19.44\ ms^{-1}$, 800 N, $0.39\ ms^{-2}$
25. 500 N, 36.9 kW
26. 35 kW, 0.73^{o}, -0.59
27. 300 N (i) $0.2\ ms^{-2}$ (ii) 255 N

<u>Exercises 3.1</u>

1. (i) 36 N (ii) $c = 1800$
2. $k = 2.74 \times 10^{5}$
3. 21 Ns

<u>Exercises 3.2</u>

1. $4.75\ ms^{-1}$, 13.7 Ns
2. $2.09\ ms^{-1}$, 0.42 Ns
3. 0.32 m
4. 1.01 s, $1.86\ ms^{-1}$,
5. 2.86 s
6. 0.36 m

Exercises 3.3

1. (a) 2 ms^{-1}, 10Ns (b) $\frac{\sqrt{13}}{2}$ ms^{-1}, $\frac{5\sqrt{13}}{2}$ Ns (c) $\sqrt{\frac{7}{2}}$ ms^{-1}, $5\sqrt{\frac{7}{2}}$ Ns

   (d) $\sqrt{3}$ ms^{-1}, $5\sqrt{3}$ Ns
2. 42 Ns, $\frac{28}{\sqrt{2}}$ Ns
3. 12 ms^{-1}, 378 J, 1.4 kg
4. $\frac{17}{60}$ s, 1.8 ms^{-1}, 3.645 J

Miscellaneous Exercises 3

1. (i) 3 ms^{-1} (ii) 3600 Ns (iii) $1333\frac{1}{3}$ kN, $533\frac{1}{3}$ N
2. $\frac{3g}{10}$, 2.6 mg, $\frac{2d}{5}$, $\frac{2}{5}\frac{\sqrt{gd}}{5}$
3. (i) $\frac{1}{2}mu\sqrt{3}$, $\frac{1}{2}u$, $\frac{1}{4}mu\sqrt{3}$, $\frac{1}{4}u\sqrt{7}$
4. (a) $\frac{m}{2}\sqrt{u^2 - ga}$ (b) $\frac{mg}{4}$ (c) $\sqrt{7ga}$
5. (i) 1.4 ms^{-1} (ii) 11.76 J (iii) 0.49 s

Exercises 4.1

1. (i) 6.36, 6.36 (ii) –7.5, 13 (iii) 6.58, –2.39 (iv) –4.1, –11.28

   (v) 1.74, –9.85
2. (i) 6.32 ms^{-1} at 71.6° to Ox (ii) 8.54 ms^{-1} at 111° to Ox

   (iii) 12.6 ms^{-1} at 71.6° below Ox (iv) 9.85 ms^{-1} at 204° to Ox

   (v) 19.21 ms^{-1} at 51.3° below Ox
3. (i) 5, $2 + 8t$ (ii) 3, $4 - 6t$ (iii) $16t$, $10t + 12t^2$ (iv) $-e^{-t}$, $-e^{-t}$ $-2e^{-2t}$
4. 18.68 ms^{-1} at 74.5° to Ox 8.54 ms^{-1} at 69.4° below Ox

Exercises 4.2

1. $4t$, $5t - 4.9t^2$, $t = 1.02$, 4.08 m
2. $6t$, $11t - 4.9t^2$, 6.17 m
3. $4t$, $12t - 4.9t^2$, 4.57 ms^{-1} at 28.8° above horizontal,

   66.5 ms^{-1} at 86.6° below horizontal
4. $21.65t$, $12.5t - 4.9t^2$, $t = 2.55$, 55.2 m
5. $24t$, $18t - 4.9t^2$, $t = 1.84$, 16.5m
6. $37.59t$, $13.68t - 4.9t^2$, 37.8 ms^{-1} at 5.9° above horizontal

   74.8 ms^{-1} at 59.9° below horizontal
7. 61.8 m
8. 2.06 m

9. 96.8 m
10. 5 ms^{-1}, 12.3 ms^{-1}
11. 19.6 ms^{-1}
12. Yes, 35.8 ms^{-1}

Miscellaneous Exercises 4

1. $20t$, $15t - 4.9t^2$, 1.53 s, 61.2 m
2. (a) (i) 4.9 s, 34.3 m (b) 83.3 m
3. (a) (i) $24t$, $32t - 4.9t^2$ (ii) –0.3 (b) 60.7 m (c) 19.6 m
4. As in 8.3, $\tan\beta = (1 - 2p)\tan\alpha$, $x_B = r(1-p)$, $a = 4hp(1-p)$
5. –2
6. 3
7. $\dfrac{gT^2}{8}$, 2
8. $\dfrac{2a}{T}$, $\dfrac{gT}{2}$
9. 9.7 ms^{-1}
10. $4g$, g
11. 27.3 ms^{-1} at 28.2° below horizontal
12. $3nut$, $5nut - \dfrac{1}{2}gt^2$, $16a - 4ut$, $17a + 3ut - \dfrac{1}{2}gt^2$, 4
13. (b) $\dfrac{3}{4}$, (c) $10.4a$
14. (a) $\tan\alpha$ $\dfrac{g}{2V^2\cos^2\alpha}$ (b) 0.2 m
15. (a) 5 s (b) 122.5 m (c) 17.5 m
16. 0.5, 3
17. $\dfrac{24v^2}{g}$, $W\sqrt{28}$
18. (b) (i) 2 (ii) 4 m (iii) 8 m (iv) 4 m

Exercises 5.1

1. (a) $\dfrac{1}{2}a$ (b) $-\dfrac{1}{2}b$, (c) $b - a$; (d) b, (e) $a - b$
   (f) $\dfrac{1}{2}(b-a)$
2. (a) $\dfrac{1}{3}a$, (b) $a + b$ (c) $b + \dfrac{1}{3}a$ (d) $-\dfrac{2}{3}a$, (e) $\dfrac{2}{3}b + \dfrac{1}{3}a$
3. (a) $-a$, (b) $-b$ (c) $a - b$ (d) $\dfrac{19}{20}b - 2a$
4. $16a - 8b$ (b) $4a+38b$ (c) $-16a + 18b$
5. (a) 6.9 at an angle of 11.44° to a (b) 24.65 at an angle of 12.8° to a

Exercises 5.2

1 (a) $x = -4, y = 1$, (b) $x = -1, y = 5$, (c) $x = 5, y = 2$

2. (a) $-5\mathbf{i}$ and $31\mathbf{j}$ (b) $-19\mathbf{i} + 9\mathbf{j}$ (c) $-3\mathbf{i} + 33\mathbf{j}$ (d) $21\mathbf{i} + 13\mathbf{j}$

3. $\mathbf{i} + 4\mathbf{j}$, $3\mathbf{i} - 2\mathbf{j}$, $-4\mathbf{i} + 3\mathbf{j}$, $-2\mathbf{i} - 6\mathbf{j}$

4. $2\mathbf{i} - 6\mathbf{j}$, $2\mathbf{i} - 9\mathbf{j}$, $-3\mathbf{i} - 10\mathbf{j}$, $-7\mathbf{i} + 5\mathbf{j}$, $-5\mathbf{i} - \mathbf{j}$

5. (a) 13, $\dfrac{5\mathrm{i} + 12\mathrm{j}}{13}$, (b) $\sqrt{53}$, $\dfrac{2\mathrm{i} + 7\mathrm{j}}{\sqrt{53}}$

(c) $\sqrt{45}$, $\dfrac{-3\mathrm{i} + 6\mathrm{j}}{\sqrt{45}}$ (d) $\sqrt{52}$, $\dfrac{-4\mathrm{i} - 6\mathrm{j}}{\sqrt{52}}$

6. (a) $2\mathbf{i} + 2\sqrt{3}\,\mathbf{j}$, (b) $-3\sqrt{3}\,\mathbf{i} + 3\mathbf{j}$, (c) $-9.4\mathbf{i} - 3.42\mathbf{j}$, (d) $2.3\mathbf{i} - 1.93\mathbf{j}$

7. (a) $\sqrt{58}$ at an angle of 66.8° to **i** in the first quadrant
(b) $\sqrt{52}$ at an angle of 56.3° to **i** in the fourth quadrant
(c) $\sqrt{29}$ at an angle of 68.2° to **i** in the second quadrant
(d) $\sqrt{80}$ at an angle of 26.6° to **i** in the third quadrant

8. (a) $25(\sqrt{3}\,\mathbf{i} + \mathbf{j})$ km, (b) $40(\sqrt{3}\,\mathbf{i} - \mathbf{j})$ km, (c) $-55\sqrt{2}\,(\mathbf{i} + \mathbf{j})$ km
(d) $37.5\,(-\sqrt{3}\,\mathbf{i} + \mathbf{j})$ km

Exercises 5.3

1. (a) $x = -2, y = 0, z = -1$, (b) $x = 2, y = 2.5, z = 2.25$, (c) $x = -3, y = 15, z = \dfrac{4}{3}$

2. (a) $30\mathbf{j} + 15\mathbf{k}$, (b) $21\mathbf{i} + 5\mathbf{j} - \mathbf{k}$ (c) $-5\mathbf{i} + 29\mathbf{j} + 13\mathbf{k}$
(d) $21\mathbf{i} - 23\mathbf{j} - 10\mathbf{k}$

3. $2\mathbf{i} + 3\mathbf{j} + 6\mathbf{k}$, $4\mathbf{i} - 3\mathbf{j} + 8\mathbf{k}$, $-5\mathbf{i} + 4\mathbf{j} - 2\mathbf{k}$, $-2\mathbf{i} + 6\mathbf{j} - 7\mathbf{k}$

4. $2\mathbf{i} - 6\mathbf{j} + 2k$, $3\mathbf{i} + 2\mathbf{j} - 5\mathbf{k}$, $-4\mathbf{i} + 3\mathbf{j} - 13\mathbf{k}$, $-7\mathbf{i} + \mathbf{j} - 8\mathbf{k}$

5. (a) 6, $\dfrac{2\mathbf{i} - \mathbf{j} + 2\mathbf{k}}{3}$, (b) $\sqrt{65}$, $\dfrac{5\mathbf{i} + 2\mathbf{j} + 6\mathbf{k}}{\sqrt{65}}$ (c) $\sqrt{61}$, $\dfrac{4\mathbf{i} + 6\mathbf{j} - 3\mathbf{k}}{\sqrt{61}}$

Exercises 5.4

1. (a) 33, (b) 46, (c) −11, (d) 7

2. (a) 12.3°, (b) 1.22° (c) 169.5° (d) 155.7°

3. (a) $7\mathbf{i} - 4\mathbf{j}$ (b) $11\mathbf{i} + 9\mathbf{j}$

4. 166°

5. (a) 68° (b) 120°

6. 5.2, 6.86

7. (a) $\dfrac{17}{5}$, $\dfrac{17}{25}(3\mathbf{i} - 4\mathbf{j})$, $\dfrac{56}{25}(4\mathbf{i} + 3\mathbf{j})$, (b) $\dfrac{69}{13}$, $\dfrac{69}{169}(12\mathbf{i} + 5\mathbf{j})$, $\dfrac{240}{169}(5\mathbf{i} - 12\mathbf{j})$

Exercises 5.5

1. (a) 38, (b) –13, (c) 16, (d) –6
2. (a) perpendicular, (b) 66.6°, (c) 4.72°, (d) perpendicular
3. 108.9°
4. $\sqrt{66}$, $\sqrt{20}$
5. $p = -\dfrac{7}{50}$
7. (a) $\dfrac{22}{3}$, $\dfrac{22}{9}(2\mathbf{i} + \mathbf{j} + 2\mathbf{k})$, $\dfrac{\mathbf{i} + 32\mathbf{j} - 17\mathbf{k}}{9}$

   (b) 1, $\dfrac{3\mathbf{i} + 4\mathbf{j} + 12\mathbf{k}}{13}$, $\dfrac{36\mathbf{i} + 87\mathbf{j} + 38\mathbf{k}}{13}$

Exercises 5.6

1. (a) $2\mathbf{i} + 20t^3\mathbf{j}$, $60t^2\mathbf{j}$ (b) $e^t\mathbf{i} + 3t^2\mathbf{j}$, $e^t\mathbf{i} + 6t\mathbf{j}$

   (c) $-\sin t\mathbf{i} + 2\cos 2t\mathbf{j}$, $-\cos t\,\mathbf{i} - 4\sin 2t\mathbf{j}$ (d) $2t\mathbf{i} + \mathbf{j} + 3t^2\mathbf{k}$, $2\mathbf{i} + 6t\mathbf{k}$

   (e) $-\sin t\mathbf{i} + 4t^3\mathbf{j} + 3\cos 3t\mathbf{k}$, $-\cos t\mathbf{i} + 12t^2\mathbf{j} - 9\sin 3t\,\mathbf{k}$

   (f) $2e^{2t}\mathbf{i} - \sin t\mathbf{j} + \dfrac{1}{t}\mathbf{k}$, $4e^{2t}\mathbf{i} - \cos t\mathbf{j} - \dfrac{1}{t^2}\mathbf{k}$
2. (a) $-\dfrac{a}{t^2}$, (b) $-a\sin t + 2tb$, (c) $e^t a - 2e^{-tb}$
3. $\dfrac{d^2 r}{dt^2} = -n^2 r$
4. (a) $t^4\mathbf{i} + t^6\mathbf{j} + \mathbf{b}$, (b) $e^{2t}\mathbf{i} + \dfrac{1^{t^3}}{3}\mathbf{j} + \mathbf{b}$, (c) $\sin 2t\mathbf{i} - \cos t\mathbf{j} + \mathbf{b}$,

   (d) $t^3\mathbf{i} + t^2\mathbf{j} + t^4\mathbf{k} + \mathbf{b}$, (e) $2\sin t\mathbf{i} + t^5\mathbf{j} - 4\cos t\mathbf{k} + \mathbf{b}$,

   (f) $e^{2t}\mathbf{i} + \sin 4t\mathbf{j} + t^2\mathbf{k} + \mathbf{b}$.
5. (a) $45\mathbf{i} + 99\mathbf{j}$, (b) $63\mathbf{i} + 6\mathbf{j} + 30\mathbf{k}$
6. (a) $\boldsymbol{r} = t^7\mathbf{i} + t^3\mathbf{j} + 3\mathbf{i} + 5\mathbf{j}$, (b) $\boldsymbol{r} = t^3\mathbf{i} + t^2\mathbf{j} + t^4\mathbf{k} + 5\mathbf{i} + 6\mathbf{j} + 7\mathbf{k}$
7. $\boldsymbol{r} = \dfrac{1}{2}t^2\boldsymbol{a} + t\boldsymbol{b} + \boldsymbol{c}$, $\boldsymbol{b}$ and $\boldsymbol{c}$ being constant vectors

Miscellaneous Exercises 5

1. (a) $(\mathbf{i} + 3\mathbf{j} + 2\mathbf{k})$m, (b) $-\mathbf{i} + 3\mathbf{j} + 2\mathbf{k}$, 31°
2. $\alpha = 2$, $\beta = 1$, $\gamma = 1$
3. $-6\mathbf{i} - \mathbf{j}$, $-\mathbf{i} + 6\mathbf{j} + 10\mathbf{k}$
4. $\sqrt{2}$, $\dfrac{\pi}{4}$
5. $6\mathbf{i} + 8\mathbf{k}$, 13, 10, 114
6. $(10 - 2\mu)\mathbf{i} + (1 + 3\mu)\mathbf{j} + (2 + 3\mu)\mathbf{k}$ $\lambda = \dfrac{3}{5}$, $\mu = \dfrac{2}{3}$
7. $\dfrac{p}{q} = \dfrac{1}{6}$

8. $\frac{1}{17}(-6\mathbf{i} - 4\mathbf{j} + 4\mathbf{k})$, $\frac{1}{17}(40\mathbf{i} - 13\mathbf{j} + 47\mathbf{k})$

9. (a) -3, (b) $\frac{4}{3}$, (c) 10, -0.4

10. 6, $\frac{2}{3}$, $-\frac{2}{3}$, $\frac{1}{3}$

11. $\frac{(\mathbf{i} - \mathbf{j})}{\sqrt{2}}$

Exercises 6.1

1. (a) $(16\mathbf{i} - 15\mathbf{j})$ N, (b) $15\mathbf{i}$ N, (c) $(9\mathbf{i} + 6\mathbf{j} + 10\mathbf{k})$ N, (d) $(10\mathbf{i} + 11\mathbf{j} - 6\mathbf{k})$ N
2. 24.8°
3. 70.5°, 35.3°
4. $23\mathbf{i} + 16\mathbf{j} + 68\mathbf{k}$
5. $(5\mathbf{i} + 10\mathbf{j})$ N, $(4\mathbf{i} + 2\mathbf{j})$ N
6. (a) $(-9\mathbf{i} + 7\mathbf{j})$ N, (b) $(-10\mathbf{i} + \mathbf{j})$ N, (c) $(-9\mathbf{i} + 4\mathbf{j})$ N, (d) $(3\mathbf{i} - 6\mathbf{j})$ N
7. (a) -2 J, (b) 66 J, (c) -15 J, (d) 16 J
8. (a) 4 J, (b) 38 J, (c) 124 J, (d) -56 J
9. $5(\mathbf{i} - \mathbf{j})$ N

Exercises 6.2

1. (a) $(42t\mathbf{i} + 8\mathbf{j})$ ms^{-2}, (b) $(4e^{-t}\,\mathbf{i} + 8e^{2t}\,\mathbf{j})$ ms^{-2}, (c) $(-16\mathbf{j} + 84t\,\mathbf{k})$ ms^{-2},
   (d) $(16e^{4t}\,\mathbf{i} - 8e^{t}\,\mathbf{j} - 14\cos t\,\mathbf{k})$ ms^{-2}
2. $(54\mathbf{i} + 45\mathbf{j})$ m
3. $(37\mathbf{i} - 35\mathbf{j})$ ms^{-1}.
4. 7.11 m
5. 17.03 ms^{-1}
6. 16.28 m
7. (a) $(3t - 300)\mathbf{i} + (210 - 6t)\mathbf{j}$, (b) $t = 48$, 174.4 m
8. 15, 150
10. $-30(1 + 2t)\mathbf{i} + 30(10t - 1)\mathbf{j} + (60t - 2)\mathbf{k}$, $t =$ 4.52 min
11. 281.1 kmh^{-1} at 84.9° S of W
12. 1.47 ms^{-1} at 28.7° N of W
13. 51.3°, 12.8 s

Exercises 6.3

1. (a) $(2.5e^{-t} + 5.5t - 0.5)\mathbf{i} + (0.75t^5 + 5t + 1)\mathbf{j}$,
   (b) $(5t^3 - 10t + 6)\mathbf{i} + (5t^4 - 26t + 14)\mathbf{j}$,
   (c) $(t^2 + 3t + 5)\mathbf{i} + \left(\frac{4}{3}t^3 - 2t - 4\right)\mathbf{j} + (4e^{2t} - 4t + 1)\mathbf{k}$,

(d) $\left(\frac{3}{2}t^2 - \frac{1}{2}\right)\mathbf{i} + (-t^3 + t + 6)\,\mathbf{j} + (t^5 - t - 2)\mathbf{k}$

2. (a) 0.82 Ns, (b) 0.85 Ns, (c) 2.47 Ns, (d) 3.93 Ns
3. (a) $(9\mathbf{i} + 24\mathbf{j})$ ms^{-1}, (b) $(6\mathbf{i} + 25\mathbf{j} + 11\mathbf{k})$ ms^{-1}
4. 4.37 Ns at 59° to direction after impact
5. (a) $t^4(0.4 + 4.9t^4)$ J, (b) $t^2(7.2 + 12.8\,t^4)$ J,
   (c) $(10\cos^2 t + 3.6\sin^2 t + 14.4\,t^2)$ J, (d) $(9t^2 + 8e^{-2t})$ J
6. (a) $(0.8t^3 + 14.4t^7)$ W, (b) $(9.6t + 86.4t^7)$ W,
   (c) $(-10.8\cos 2t\sin 2t + 45\sin 3t\cos 3t + 21.6t)$ W, (d) $(50t - 144e^{-4t})$ W
7. (a) 5.3 J, (b) $14.4\pi^2$ J

Miscellaneous Exercises 6

1. (a) $-m\,\mathbf{i}$ Ns, (b) $\frac{1}{2}m(1 + \pi^2)$ J, (c) $2m(\mathbf{i} - \pi\mathbf{j})$ N, (d) $2m(1 + \pi^2)$ W
2. (a) $10\frac{2}{3}$
3. (a) $[2(\pi a\cos\pi t + 2bt)\mathbf{i} + (-\pi c\sin\pi t + 2dt)\mathbf{j}]$ Ns,
   (b) $[(\pi a\cos\pi t + 2bt)^2 + (-\pi c\sin\pi t + 2dt)^2]$ J,
   (c) $[2(-\pi^2 a\sin\pi t + 2b)\mathbf{i} + (-\pi^2 c\cos\pi t + 2d)\mathbf{j}]$ N
   $a = -4$, $b = 20$, $c = \frac{4}{\pi}$, $d = 4$, power $= 160(\pi^2 + 10)$ W
4. 18 J, 3 ms^{-1}
5. (a) $t = \frac{\pi}{2}, \frac{3\pi}{2}$ ..... (b) $t = 0, \frac{\pi}{2}, \frac{3\pi}{2}$ .... (c) $t = \frac{\pi}{4}, \frac{5\pi}{4}, \frac{9\pi}{4}$, ...
6. $(2.4\cos 2t\,\mathbf{i} + 8e^{4t}\,\mathbf{j})$ N, $(7.2\sin 2t\cos 2t + 40e^{8t})$ W
7. (a) $(4\cos 4t\,\mathbf{i} - 4\sin 4t\,\mathbf{j} + 2t\,\mathbf{k})\text{ms}^{-1}$, $(-16\sin 4t\,\mathbf{i} - 16\cos 4t\,\mathbf{j} + 2\mathbf{k})\text{ms}^{-2}$,
   (b) $0.8t$ W
8. (a) $\frac{2\mathbf{i} + \mathbf{j} - 2\mathbf{k}}{3}$, (b) 4 N, (c) 36 J
9. (a) $(0.7\mathbf{i} + 6.3\mathbf{j})$ Ns, (b) 12.6 J
10. (a) $(14\mathbf{i} + 3\mathbf{j} + 12\mathbf{k})$ N, (b) $\sqrt{349}$ N, (c) 71, (d) 0.75, (e) 87 J
11. (a) $(\mathbf{i} + \cos t\,\mathbf{j})$ ms^{-2}, (b) $\left(\frac{t^2}{2}\mathbf{i} - \cos t\,\mathbf{j} + 4\mathbf{i} + 4\mathbf{j}\right)$ m
12. (a) $(2\mathbf{i} - 12\sin 3t\,\mathbf{j} + 12\cos 3t\,\mathbf{k})$ ms^{-1}, (b) $t = \frac{1}{2}$
13. (b) 300 kmh^{-1}, (c) $(11 - 2t)^2 + (1 + t)^2 + 9t^2$, $t = 1.5$
14. $[(3 - t)\mathbf{i} + (12 + 3t - kt)\,\mathbf{j}]$ m, (a) $k = 7$, $t = 3$, (b) $\frac{15}{2}, \frac{9}{\sqrt{2}}$ m, $3 \le t \le 12$
15. (a) 1.3 J, (b) 0.33
16. (a) $(-0.3\mathbf{i} + 2.1\mathbf{j})$ Ns, (b) 18.9 J
17. (a) $(3\cos t\,\mathbf{i} - 5\sin t\,\mathbf{j})$ ms^{-1}, 5, 3, (b) $\frac{8}{17}$, (c) $4.8\sin t\cos t$ W, 2.4 W

18. $-0.4\pi(\cos\pi t\,\mathbf{i}+\sin\pi t\,\mathbf{j})$ N, $[b+t(-6\mathbf{i}+8\mathbf{j})]$ m, $3\mathbf{i}+\left(\frac{2}{\pi}-4\right)\mathbf{j}$

19. (a) $\frac{u}{5}(3\mathbf{i}+4\mathbf{j})\,t$ km, $[10(-\mathbf{i}+\mathbf{j})+10t\,\mathbf{i}]$ km,

(b) $u=\frac{50}{7}$, 1.45 p.m. (c) (ii) 1.30 p.m. (iii) 12.30 p.m.

20. (a) $[(30-40t)\,\mathbf{i}+(20+pt)\mathbf{j}+10\mathbf{k}]$ km,

$[(-10+120t)\mathbf{i}+200t\,\mathbf{j}+(15+qt)\mathbf{k}]$ km,

(b) $p=120$, $q=-20$

Exercises 7.1

1. $x=kt$
2. $x=[2(k-t)]^{-\frac{1}{2}}$
3. $v=(k-3t)^{\frac{1}{3}}$
4. $r=\dfrac{k}{\cos\theta}$
5. $x=4e^{t}$
6. $x=(27-2t)^{\frac{1}{2}}$
7. $x=\dfrac{4}{5-t^4}$
8. $y=\ln(2-e^{x})$
9. $v=\frac{4}{3}-\frac{1}{3}e^{-3t}$
10. $v=\frac{4}{3}-\frac{11}{3}e^{-3t}$
11. $y=\sqrt{1+(x+2)^2}$

Exercises 7.2

1. 200
2. $r=k\ln s+c$
3. 0.31
4. 1.04 × number in population
5. 50238
6. £598.61
7. 25°
8. 1.8 units
9. $\dfrac{dx}{dt}=2x-0.01x^2$, $x=\dfrac{200}{1+39e^{-2t}}$

Miscellaneous Exercises 7

1. $\dfrac{3n}{4}$

2. (a) $x = 1000 + ae^{0.1t}$, (i) $x = 1000 - 100\,e^{0.1t}$, (ii) $x = 1000 + 100e^{0.1t}$

   (b) $x = 10000e^{at+\frac{1}{2}bt^2}$ 0.235

3. $y = \tan\left(\dfrac{x^5}{5} + x\dfrac{\pi}{4} - 630\right)$

4. $\dfrac{1}{15}\ln 2$

5. 238 minutes

6. $p = \dfrac{1}{10+90e^{-0.001t}}$, 0.1

INDEX